LIFE AFTER FIFTY

LIFE AFTER FIFTY

J. C. MORETTI

Ordering Information:

 BookTrail Agency
8838 Sleepy Hollow Rd.
Kansas City, MO 64114

Printed in the United States of America

Contents

PART 1
The Life of Charlie

Chapter 1

Summer 1979

I woke to the heavy sigh of the ash trees as they swished in the early morning breeze. I still have the child-like expectation of a 'do nothing or absolutely anything adventure sort of day'

We lived in the Black Country in a place called Dudley. My father would always remind us that the Black Country gained its name in the mid-nineteenth century due to the smoke from the many thousands of ironworking foundries and forges, plus also the working of the shallow and thirty-foot thick coal seams.

It was 1979, and by midday, my father would be complaining that we were fetching tar off the bloody streets on our shoes. 'I don't spend every day sweating my cobs off on a tar truck at spaghetti junction for you two to fetch it home with you from the lane.'

'Charlie, Jack, take them bloody shoes off and leave them outside.'

Dad clipped us on the head, but we knew he loved us with every fibre of his being.

Our mom was not yet thirty-four, with two small kids, a tiny council house, and unable to walk to her own front door without using a walker. Muscular dystrophy struck her hard after giving birth to us. She was cared for by our doting father, who barely slept, worked nights, and spent his days caring for our mom. Our sister, whom we hardly saw, seven years older than I, would stay at nans house most of the time.

What did we care? This was our normal. Mom worshipped dad, dad worshipped mom, and they doted on us. Love was never in short supply in our tiny council house.

Worn out shoes, jumble sale clothes, and a weekly trip to the library for free books were our normal. To say that expectations were low for our futures would be an understatement. But Maggy Thatcher gave us milk and lunch at school, and our dad had a hot dinner on the table at 5.00 pm every night without fail.

After our dinner, Jack and I would thank him for our meal and help clear and wash up for him; the evening was then ours. I was eight years old, my brother was five years old, and we ran around with the other kids from our estate. Making dens out of willow branches along the railway sidings. Listening to the Bay City Rollers on Jason's parents' dad's transistor, life was sweet. The grass was so sunburnt its scent was pure sweet summertime to us. Even now, reaching fifty, if I drive through the countryside during the harvest, I stop, close my eyes, inhale deeply, and I am transported deeply back to that glorious summer. Jason's dad would whack him hard for taking his transistor radio during the cricket season, but it was worth every bruise and black eye to Jase because to us, he was a hero.

Twelve years old to my eight, he knew it all. He would steel his dad's copy of 'readers wives' and show us pictures of naked women with huge breasts, huge permed hair, and massive pubic triangles.

I felt excited and squirmy but had no idea what these feelings were or where they would lead me.

If you strip a willow branch and stab the shoots into the earth, they will grow. Our hangout headquarters provided a secret cool place to hide away from the scorching sun, Jason's dad, and all life's trials and tomorrows. But life has a way of changing shape, stealing hope, and robbing dreams. But just like pandora's box in Aesop's fable, when despair is released, hope will always follow it. Jason began coughing hard at the end of July. His skin, usually tanned and ruddy, was looking was grey, sweaty, and pallid. Then, one day when we called for him after tea, his mom answered the door.

'Jason won't be coming out to play.'

'Why?' we asked

He is at the Queen Elizabeth hospital; Jason has cancer.' She sobbed

Six weeks later, our willow gang stood next to our parents and watched as Jason's coffin was lowered into the ground. We never visited our willow den again. Eight years later, a shortcut through the railway siding left me with a very different memory.

Chapter 2
Spring 1987

It was the late Bank Holiday, Monday, the end of May, and the sun shone through my bedroom curtains; it was only 6.00 am. I had studied and revised all weekend in anticipation of my 'O' Levels in June. I had set my alarm for 6.00 am so that I could study in bed from 6.00 am until early afternoon. I found I always studied better first thing, and by the afternoon, I would then have time to hang around with my friends. I opened the curtains and got my head into my books whilst still lying in bed. My dad bought snacks up to my room and cups of tea to keep me going.

I had started my period a few days earlier, my spots were clearing up, and I didn't feel as drained as I did at the start of my period. At least I wasn't at school anymore. I hated having to do sports when I was on my period. I always remember getting a letter from my parents to permit me not to have to get in the shower with all the other girls.

By around 2.00 pm, I had had enough. I found after eight hours, I didn't take much more information into my brain. I packed up my books, made my bed, and had a hot shower. By 3.00 pm, I was ready to go out and meet my friends. At sixteen, I could stay out until 10.00 pm; that was my curfew. I had friends who lived about twenty minutes away, and we would all hang out together in a park not far from the railway I used to hang out on with Jason as a younger child.

I remember on this bank holiday, the afternoon was very warm, the sun was scorching, just as I remembered as a child playing out with Jason. I wore some light turquoise leggings and a thin top. I was very slim and had long, dark, naturally curly hair. I was into Madonna, so I wore lace in my hair and lacey gloves. I thought I was the bee's knees as I set off to meet my mates. I put my Walkman on, listening to Madonna as I walked. I had put red lipstick on and scrunched my hair in a messy look. I thought I looked so cool. I walked for a few minutes through a couple of villages, then down an alleyway as a shortcut to a main road. I remember listening to 'Like a Virgin' by Madonna, as happy as larry, looking forward to seeing my mates.

As I got halfway down the alley, I saw a shadow at the side of me coming from behind. I turned around to see a young gentleman around twenty or twenty-one years of age. He wore a grey hoody with the hood over his head and blue jeans. I smiled, thinking he would overtake me. He walked at the same pace as me down the last bit of the alley, then seemed to get a pace up and disappeared, or so I thought. As I reached the end of the alley, close to the railway line, he jumped out and startled me. I still had my music on with the earplugs in my ears. I instantly pulled the earphones away from my ears. The man grabbed hold of me, pulling me down to the ground. I hadn't a clue what was going on and started to scream.

'If you want to stay alive, do as I fucking say,' he said.

He pulled me up off the ground, back onto my legs, dragging me along with him, tugging at my arms. He held my arms so tight that they started to bruise. We got to the top of the railway where I had always played with Jas as a kid. He turned for the railway and started to pull me down the small lane heading for the railway lines. I knew something bad was going to happen. I felt the tears begin to stroll down my face.

I pulled back so hard, struggling with the man to get away, begging him to let me go. He was so much stronger than me. He punched me so hard in the face, I felt this huge bang to the side of my face, which knocked me for six to the floor. I got on all fours on the floor to get up, but before I could get up, he grabbed me by my hair and pulled me further down towards the railway.

I sobbed, knowing the farther I got from the main road, the less chance anyone could hear me. My hands and legs were bleeding from being dragged on the ground, the cuts and nerve fibres in my body signalled to my brain the amount of pain I was feeling. I sobbed and sobbed, knowing there was nowhere to escape.

'Shut up, bitch, else I'll give you something to cry for,' he shouted.

I could not believe that this was happening on a sunny May bank holiday in the middle of the afternoon. Why me? Why did no one hear me? What was going to happen to me?

We got down to the railway line, and I could barely see out of my eyes, for the tears and the pain I felt where I had been punched and dragged were crucifying. I was petrified, wondering whether I would get out of this alive. Now on the railway line, no one could see or hear me.

He pulled me close to him by my hair, my body was shaking with fear, and the tears strolled down my face.

He repeated, shouting in my face, 'I'll give you something to cry for if you don't fucking shut up.'

'Please let me go,' I sobbed.

He yanked at my leggings trying to pull them down. I tried so hard to fight back and push him away. The man was much stronger than I, and the more I fought back, the more violent he got, punching and kicking me. I felt blood running down my face from a punch; he had a ring on that caught my face. Ignoring the blood on my face, again, he pulled on my leggings to pull them down. I was on my period and wore a pad.

'I'm on my period,' I cried.

He ignored me and carried on, blinkered to what I had said.

Everything was in a daze; it felt like I was having a nightmare and would wake up from it all. I started to feel sick as he pulled the leggings to my knees, I felt degraded, embarrassed, and ashamed. As he started to pull at my pants, he could see I had a pad on and stopped. I don't think he believed I was on my period. What was he going to do next, I feared? I continued sobbing.

He then pushed me down on to the floor onto my knees. As I fell, I quickly pulled my leggings up. I wiped my face with my arm. I looked to see dirt and blood all over my arm from my face. I don't think he noticed me pulling up my leggings whilst on the ground. He was too busy undoing his trousers. His trousers dropped to the floor, I noticed he had red checked boxer shorts on. He looked at me and smiled whilst pulling them down to his knees.

My whole body was shaking, I felt totally hopeless. I thought if I had not put all that make-up on and worn the lacy clothing, this would not be happening. It must have been something I had done. By now, his penis was on show, and he started to masturbate with one hand whilst still grabbing my hair with his other hand so that I couldn't run away. I thought I would die and that my body would be left on the railway line for somebody to find.

As he masturbated faster and faster, he pulled my head to his penis and pushed it hard into my mouth. I started to heave and gag; this wasn't something I had ever done before or even dreamt of doing. Vomit came into my mouth, and I had to swallow it again.

'Suck it, bitch, if you want to live,' he said.

I didn't for one minute disbelieve what he said, he was violent. I did exactly what he said whilst closing my eyes to think about the good times on the railway as a kid with Jas. Good memories of the spot were all I had to hold onto right now, it helped relieve some of the pain.

What happened next was a distant memory, I tried to block it out, all I recall was him pushing his penis faster and faster into my mouth until he ejaculated. I remember pulling away and vomiting on the floor. I had a salty taste, which was revolting. The question was, what was he going to do next? Surprisingly, he dressed himself, stood in front of me, and said,

'If you tell anyone about this, I'll come after you. I know where you live, and I know about your family.'

I was still on my knees on the ground. I looked at him, my body still shaking with shock and fear. I held back the tears as I didn't want to annoy him.

'Are you listening to me, bitch? You wanted this,' he said.

I nodded my head and agreed. 'I promise I won't say anything.'

I wanted to survive and would have agreed to anything. On that, he turned and ran off along the railway. I left it five minutes before I got up. I wanted to make sure he had gone. Shortly after, I ran across the railway line back up to the main street. I couldn't see anyone; it was bank holiday Monday and very quiet on the roads. I ran so fast through the streets to the park where my friends were, the tears strolled down my face as I reached the park, my friends were on the swings waving to me as I ran closer.

'Where have you been,' Karen shouted.

As I got closer, she could see something had happened.

'Oh my god, Charlie, what's happened? Look at the state of you, you're all bleeding and cut.'

I was in a state of shock, still sobbing so much that I couldn't get my words out, eventually, I said, 'I've been raped, Karen,' I said as I collapsed on the ground.

Karen sat next to me on the floor and put her arms around me, hugging me. On that, two other friends came running over.

Karen shouted, 'Go to the telephone box now and call the police, we need them here now. Charlie has been raped. I'll stay with her'. Karen knew I couldn't talk and was in a state of shock.

Karen hugged me tighter. 'It's okay, Charlie. The police will be here shortly; you'll be fine.'

My body carried on shaking, and I still couldn't talk. Before no time, the police turned up with blue flashing lights. A female and male police officer came over to me, they both leant closely down to me and showed empathy towards me.

'Okay, Charlie, I believe from your friends there has been a sexual incident.'

I nodded, still sobbing.

'It's okay,' they responded, 'we will get whoever is responsible for this.'

'No, he'll kill me,' I sobbed.

'He won't, Charlie, you are in safe hands.' The policewoman took my hand and held me tight, taking over from Karen.

She spoke quietly, 'I want you to come to the station, Charlie. I know it's hard, but we need to understand what has happened and take a statement while it's still fresh in your memory.'

I cried, 'I need to tell my family; I won't be home in time for 10.00 pm, and they'll worry.'

'It's okay, Charlie, when we have all your details, we will contact your parents. I am from CID, and I am going to help you. Will you come to the station to help us?' she asked.

She held my hand. 'We're going to help you through this and catch the suspect, but we need you to cooperate. Do you understand, Charlie?'

I nodded. Karen and my other friends watched as I got up off the ground. Being led to the police car, they all blew a kiss at me. 'You will be okay, Charlie, be brave, we love you lots.'

I headed off to the local police station in the police car. The officers in charge were in normal clothes, making me feel more at ease. They seemed to have a knack to ask where I lived and my home telephone number without me even realising I'd given it to them. When we arrived at the station, they got me a cup of tea and tried to make jokes with me to keep my mind on other things. They must have contacted my family whilst doing this.

'Your father is on the way, Charlie; he won't be long.' They sat with me all the time until my dad arrived.

CHAPTER 3

1987
AFTER THE EVENT

'Your dad's here with your sister. Charlie. Is it okay to call them in?' the CID officer asked.

We were in a kind of canteen, not an interview room, which made me feel more at ease.

Both walked in, and my sister burst into tears. I saw tears in my dad's eyes, too; they both hugged me tightly.

We all sobbed, and they held me tightly. I knew my dad was struggling with it. I was still his baby girl. My mom, still battling muscular dystrophy, stayed at home with my younger brother. It was a struggle for her to walk these days.

I had never talked about sex to my dad, so this was difficult for us. The police asked if I would make a statement. I asked if my sister could be present; I thought it would be too embarrassing for both my dad and I if he was present.

It was done very informally in a room at the police station. The room was one they would use to question criminals, albeit I didn't feel under arrest. I talked whilst one police officer took notes, and the other asked me questions to get me to elaborate more to not miss out on anything critical for the investigation. My sister, seven years older, sat with me and held my hand, I didn't want my dad to hear the gory details. We both cried as I unreeled the details. After taking a statement from me, the police explained that they needed an examination and would need to take some photographic evidence of my injuries.

I remember having to strip off, and one by one, they placed each item of clothing into forensic bags. They then explained that they needed a forensic doctor to take an examination inside my vaginal area.

'Why do I need to have this done when I've told you I didn't have intercourse?' I cried

'It's evidence for your case, Charlie. We need a doctor to substantiate your statement,' the policewoman replied.

Firstly, the police photographed my injuries, face, arms, and legs, where I was badly bruised and cut.

I had never been through anything like this in my life; my sister still held my hand whilst they did an internal swab. I felt like the victim. My dignity was gone. The doctor confirmed to the police that I was a sixteen-year-old virgin, had never had sexual intercourse, and was on my monthly period.

I was so relieved when it was all over, and they said I could go home. My sister had brought some fresh clothes with her for me to change into. Whilst I got dressed, the police explained to my dad that they would see what DNA evidence they had, call out for any witnesses, start to build a case, and search for the criminal.

The policewoman offered to drive us home. We didn't have a car. It was a luxury in those days to have a car.

My mom hugged me. I knew she wanted to be with me, but muscular dystrophy prevailed and made that difficult. We never talked about sex as a family at all, so this was a difficult subject to approach. I knew my parents were hurting as much as me.

I wanted a hot bath when I got home, somewhere I could be on my own. I sat in the hot water and cried and scrubbed myself, still asking why me and wondering what would have happened if I had been killed. This really messed with my mind, and I'm not sure my parents knew how to support me. Who would?

The following day, the CID telephoned early and asked if they could pick me up and go to the crime scene. My heart sank as the thought of going back to the railway line disturbed me, yet, I had had so much fun there as a child.

The police picked me up at about 11.00 am, and we drove to the scene. There was a forensic team in white outfits waiting for us at the top of the railway line when we arrived. I felt sick and didn't really know what was going on. I just went along with it, still in a tranche from the day before. I guided the police down to the railway line where the incident had happened. It was not a place I would ever forget, from a child to this. I soon led them to the place where you could see the vomit on the floor from myself. I cried hysterically as I stood there, the dreadful memories came rushing back.

My dad and sister stood at the side whilst the policewoman consoled me. I watched as the police cautioned off the area, and tape was put around the scene. It was all cautioned off at the entrance from pedestrians. My dad and sister held my hand and hugged me to help me feel safe. I kept thinking that it was my fault and could I, should I, have done something differently. Shortly after I had identified the spot, the police dropped us home. They didn't want to keep me there longer than they had to

'You don't need to be here now, Charlie. Leave the rest to the police.'

As I walked away from the scene, the forensic team had swabs and bags in their hands, bending down to the spot; others were taking photographs. It was like something I'd watched in the Sweeney when I was younger.

As the investigation continued, I hardly went outdoors. I locked myself inside and went very inward. I studied for my exams but never attended any revision classes at school. I could never face getting the bus to school on my own in open places, not even during the afternoons. My mother explained it to the school, who was really understanding and sent work home to me. The investigation continued over the weeks to try to find the criminal. My incident was in the local newspapers, but my name was never disclosed because of being a minor.

I rarely went out these days, only to sit for my exams. I panicked that the guy who raped me knew where I lived and would come after my family or me as he promised. The nightmare lived with me for weeks, and I barely slept.

I had just gotten through my exams in June when there was a breakthrough. Somebody came forward and said the man had been bragging about the rape in a local pub to friends after consuming a lot of alcohol. The gang laughed about it with him. The man was tracked down by the police and arrested for questioning. His semen matched that found on my clothes, and his blood and DNA was also found on my clothing. He was charged and kept in custody; I was so relieved when he was held in prison and off the streets. He couldn't come after me while he was locked up.

The police told me he had pleaded not guilty. His allegation was that I went along with it and wanted sex; however, he was still retained in custody. This tormented my mind, and I became very depressed in the coming months, again questioning what I did wrong. Did I wear the wrong clothes? Did I dress inappropriately? Was it my fault? I didn't feel like the victim.

As time went on, he still pleaded not guilty and blamed everything on me. The police explained that it would have to go to the court, where I would have to give evidence for the trial. I wasn't sure I could re-live the trial again, and believe me, it was a trial.

As summer moved on, I became in a depressed state, worried sick about the court case set for the middle of August. The day before the trial, I noticed a police car pull up outside the house. I assumed they had come to go over my statement one last time before the trial. I let them in the house, one was the CID policewoman who had worked on my case from the start. I liked her; she showed a lot of empathy and supported me all through this ordeal. She smiled at me as she entered the house and touched me on my arm.

'I have some good news for you, Charlie,' she said as she sat down

She went on to say, 'He has changed his plea today to guilty.'

Tears rolled down my face as my parents smiled and held my hand.

'What does that mean?' I asked.

'It means you don't have to go to court; we have enough evidence, and it should be a straightforward sentencing tomorrow.'

I was so relieved; I hadn't got to live the ordeal again and see the man who had put me through it. As the police left, she held my arm.

'We'll call you tomorrow to let you know the outcome.'

The following day, on the same day of the court case, my exam results arrived in the post. Typical it was the same day, was this an omen? I thought. I was pleasantly surprised to read that I had passed all my exams all with Grade A and B's. I don't know how I managed it with all the distractions in my life, but I did. I was thrilled, and it meant I could go on to the college I wanted in September to study finance and business studies.

I moped around for the rest of the day wondering how the case was going. I had butterflies in my tummy waiting to hear the outcome.

Later that day, I got more good news about the court case.

The CID officer telephoned. 'Charlie, good news; he was charged with attempted rape and sexual assault. The prosecutor questioned why a teenage virgin on their period would go to a railway line with a stranger to perform sexual activities. There was enough semen and vomit as evidence. They also had enough circumstantial evidence from your torn clothes and pictures of your injuries. They sentenced him to seven years and have moved him to Winson Green prison in Birmingham.'

I was so relieved when I got the call, this time I cried with relief.

'You can put closure to it now Charlie, he got what he deserved, and you can start to move on with your life.'

Today was the end of a chapter in my life, and for the first time in months, I looked forward to a new start at college in September.

Chapter 4
Meeting Sebastian

It was Monday 7th September 1987, my first day at college. It was a little scary, and the college was a million times bigger than my school. It was funny not to get a chance to see any old faces, but I met loads of nice new people. I didn't have to wear a uniform either, result, I hated my school uniform, I wore jeans, a t-shirt, and trainers.

When I arrived, there was no register. They asked my name on arriving and what course I was studying. They ticked my name off on a sheet of paper and guided me to a large room where there were lots of other students. You could see we were all nervous. Why wouldn't we be? We were all so young. I sat next to a girl who was chatty

'Hi, I'm Robyn, are you studying finance and business studies?'

'I am, yes, oh, and I'm Charlie.'

Robyn smiled at me; she was the new first friend I made.

Shortly after arriving, we had a tour of the college. It was huge. There was a huge library, dining room, and gym and sports area; it was amazing, so different from school. I walked into the gym. I had never used one before, never had to. I was the perfect size ten with long, dark, curly hair. I spotted a guy using a weight machine. He stared over at me and never stopped watching me. We continued with the induction, telling us the times the gym was open and the rules of using the gym.

As we left, I looked back at the guy. He looked so handsome. He had dark, thick hair, rather curly on top but cut shorter at the bottom. He was very muscular and slim, nothing like the boys from school.

Our induction continued, and we left the gym and sports centre and headed back to classroom. The next thing was to get passes. I had my photograph taken and a plastic pass issued to me to use as my ID to get into the college. I was given a timetable of all my lectures for the week; this included free time to study. I enjoyed my first day, and I felt like an adult. The atmosphere was different. I was treated like an adult, and it was my choice to attend lectures.

The second day was even better. I had my first lectures. I sat next to Robyn. She was a chatterbox and made me laugh. At lunch, I encountered into the dining area on my own. I hadn't brought a lunch with me. Robyn had some sandwiches, and she said she was going to sit outside with her lunch. She asked me to join her if I wished, once I had got some lunch.

The dining area was very busy. I looked at what food was available. There were delicious sandwiches, jacket potatoes, and hot food. I looked over and noticed the guy from the gym from the previous day sitting with a group of boys. They were all dressed in designer shorts and tops. He looked just as handsome as the day before. He looked over and spotted me looking at him. I looked away immediately.

As I grabbed a sandwich from the food bar, I heard a voice.

'The food is good in here, that's one of the best sandwiches you've chose, very healthy.'

I looked behind me to see the guy who had been staring at me standing there. He looked even more handsome up closely. He was about six foot and towered over me. I had chosen a freshly prepared chicken salad sandwich.

I smiled at him. 'Yes, it's very different to the meals we got at school.'

'Too true, what are you studying?'

'Finance and business studies. How about you?'

'Nice course. I'm not as brainy as you; I'm studying sports and nutrition.'

'I wouldn't say that I'm brainy at all. I thought you looked fit; goes with the course, I suppose.'

'You're fit too.' I took that as a compliment

He went on to say, 'There's a few of us from school doing the same course, so it's not as daunting for me. How about you?'

By now, I had got to the checkout to pay for my sandwich and was sorting some money out my bag to pay.

'I don't know anyone, so it's very daunting for me but it's okay, and I'm enjoying it so far.'

He smiled at me. 'My name is Sebastian.'

'My name is Charlotte; my friends call me Charlie.'

I moved on in the queue to get some sauces for my sandwich whilst Sebastian was paying for his lunch. He was soon at my side again.

'You can join us for lunch if you'd like.'

'I'm not sure. You're with all your mates.'

'No, please sit with me; don't be on your own.'

I smiled. 'Okay then.'

His eyes were bright blue, and he was so good looking. We sat down at a table next to his friends. He shouted, 'Everyone, this is Charlie.'

'Hi, Charlie,' they shouted back. They seemed like a decent bunch for a group of boys. After all, we were all in the same boat; this was our first week and we were finding our way around college life.

Sebastian and I talked whilst eating our lunch. I found out we were the same age. We talked about what schools we had been to, where we lived, and our interests. The time went so fast, before I knew it, it was time to get to my next lecture.

'Sorry, Sebastian. I must go; I have a lecture in five minutes and not sure where the room is.'

'No problem, Charlie, you have a great afternoon, and maybe I'll see you here tomorrow for lunch again.'

I smiled as I stood. He stood to see me off and winked. What a gentleman, I thought as I went off to find my room. The rest of the day went very fast. Robyn was great; she was chatty which made me feel at ease.

The following day was just as good. I had a fantastic lecture first thing, then free study time from 11.00 am. I sat in the dining area with Robyn, and we shared our notes and worked on some assignments. Before I knew it, the dining room started to fill up; it was lunch time. I kept looking at the door for Sebastian. Sebastian and his friends walked in around 12.30 pm. I was over in the corner with Robyn. I saw him looking round the room, then he spotted me, waved, and winked. Sebastian was so charming. Today he was dressed in Nike shorts and a matching t-shirt, showing off his biceps. He led his friends over to a table next to Robyn and me.

'Hi, ladies, are you having lunch?'

'I have a homemade chicken salad with me today, Sebastian.'

Robyn replied, 'I have food with me, too.'

Sebastian smiled. 'Well excuse me, ladies, whilst I go and grab something.'

Robyn looked at me. 'Where do you know him from?'

'Only from college, since yesterday.'

'Really? He's very hot. He's got the hots for you, Charlie.'

Sebastian and his friends got their food and came over to sit with us. One of Sebastian's friends hit off with Robyn, and they started flirting, result, I thought. Sebastian chatted with me all the way through lunch. He showed interest and complimented me regularly.

This carried on all year. Robyn and I had so much fun. Robyn started to date a friend of Sebastian's, and Sebastian and I grew closer and closer. I had butterflies whenever we met up. I knew he was the one for me; he was the kindest, gentlest person I'd ever met. We started to meet up outside college in December. We went to the cinema and met up on weekends with friends for drinking sessions in pubs, then onto night clubs.

It was Christmas eve in 1987, and we all went night clubbing. Robyn was still all loved up with one of Sebastian's friends. We danced and drank the night away; I enjoyed the night so much and had so much fun. At the end of the night, the music slowed down, and Sebastian asked me to dance. He took my hand and led me to the dance floor. He put his arms around me, and we danced together to a song called 'Perfect Day' by Lou Reed; it was so romantic.

Halfway through the song, Sebastian held my hands, looked into my eyes, and said,

'I really like you, Charlie; I think I'm falling in love with you. You are the one I want to marry.' We had seen each other every day for almost four months.

I felt so emotional in a happy way, and for the first time, I knew I was in love. I looked into his eyes, and we kissed and snogged each other for the remainder of the song. I knew he was the one.

It was pouring heavily with rain when we left the club. Sebastian wrapped his coat around me and held me in his arms while we waited for a taxi.

He whispered in my ear 'There's no one at home if you want to stay over at mine. There's a spare bedroom for you to stay in.'

I didn't take much persuading. 'Are you sure? It would be nice, but it's Christmas tomorrow.'

'That's fine. I couldn't think of anything better than seeing you Christmas morning.'

We got a taxi back to Sebastian's. The house was rather posh compared to where I had come from; it wasn't a council house with a huge driveway and pretty leaded windows. We were both soaking wet from the rain. Sebastian got one of his bath robes for me to change into. I went to the bathroom and changed into it and washed my face; when I got back, the fire was lit and there was a glass of wine on the side waiting for me. Sebastian had changed into different bath robe.

He smiled at me. 'Come sit here.'

I sat on the sofa next to him, and we continued drinking and laughing. He put my glass down, held my chin, and started kissing me. The kissing got intense, and he started to move his hands towards my breasts. I stopped him for a minute

'Sebastian, I'm a virgin. I've never done this before, I thought you should know, I'm a bit nervous.'

'Charlie, I'm a virgin too; this is the first for me. I'm sorry if I'm going to fast, we don't have to do anything you don't want to do. I really like you; I don't care if I have to wait until the day I marry you.'

I knew after that we would be together forever and get married. He was so sweet. It felt wonderful that we were both virgins and this was the first time for both of us. I pulled him back towards me, and we started kissing again. Shortly after, he got up and carried me upstairs to his bedroom. He dropped me on his bed and slowly slid the robe off me, I did the same to him. We kissed and snogged for about five minutes, then he put his hand between my legs. I think I was already wet, but he felt his way inside me with one finger.

'Are you okay, Charlie? Tell me to stop if there is anything you don't like; I want you to feel comfortable and happy.'

I pulled him back to me and we started snogging again. He moved his finger out and guided his penis inside me; it took us a while to get it in, I must admit it did hurt me.

'It's hurting, Sebastian.'

'Okay, I'll go slower.' He laughed. 'Maybe it's my size.'

I laughed out loud. 'I'll be the judge of that.'

'Seriously, Charlie, tell me if you want to stop.'

'I'm okay.'

Sebastian moved slowly inside me and only pushed deeper the wetter I got. He kissed my neck and felt my breasts. We were both nervous; it was the first time for us, and we didn't know what to expect. Every few minutes he asked, 'Are you okay, Charlie?'

He was so caring and thoughtful, all he wanted to do was make sure I was comfortable and not in pain.

We started to breathe heavy, and I felt a change in my body. I got butterflies.

'I think I'm going to come, Sebastian.'

'Oh, me too Charlie. I'm glad you said that.'

He pushed harder for a few seconds, and I screamed.

'I've come, Charlie.'

Sebastian lay on top of me for ages after. His penis eventually softened and slipped out of me.

'Sebastian, it's going everywhere.'

'I'll get some tissues.'

He jumped out of bed and came running back with tissues.

'Here you go, Charlie.'

We wiped ourselves and cleaned up.

We got back in Sebastian's bed, snuggling up to each other. He held me tight in his arms. I felt so loved up. It was the happiest I had felt in a long time.

I awoke about 9.00 am. We had drunk a few drinks the night before, and my head was sore. I could hear Christmas songs playing. I turned over, and Sebastian wasn't there. Just on that he walked back into the bedroom

'Merry Christmas, Charlie.'

'Merry Christmas, Sebastian.'

He carried a tray with a cooked breakfast on it and a pot of tea. My goodness, I had never been spoilt like this before. There was bacon, eggs, mushrooms, beans, and toast. He placed it on the side and kissed me on the cheek.

'Sebastian, this is lovely, where's yours?'

'I'm going to get it; I'll be back in a sec.'

He went downstairs and came back with his tray with the same food on it. He dropped his bathrobe to get back in bed. I looked at him; what an amazing body he had. He got back in bed, and we ate our breakfast, laughing and joking. Christmas songs were blaring out across the house. 'So here it is Merry Christmas' was playing by Slade. After we had finished eating, we placed our trays on the side cabinets. I was so full.

Sebastian pulled me to him, and we kissed intimately again.

'I have another surprise for you, Charlie.'

'Ohh, what's that then; you're full of surprises.'

He reached his hand down to the side of his bed and picked up a gift-wrapped present in the most gorgeous Christmas paper and handed it to me.

'This is for you, Charlie. I hope you like it. If not, don't worry I can change it.'

I carefully opened the gift and saw it was a ring box. As I opened it, Sebastian looked at me to explain 'It's an eternity ring, Charlie. I don't know how you feel, but I wanted to get something like that, something meaning for my love for you.'

Before he finished, I said, 'I love it, Sebastian, it's beautiful.'

The ring was a white gold, V-shaped diamond ring. He couldn't have chosen anything better.

Sebastian put it on my finger. I was ecstatic with excitement. This was the best Christmas ever, it fit perfectly. I felt guilty. I hadn't got Sebastian a present. I didn't tell him that.

'I have a gift for you, Sebastian, it's at...'

Before I could finish, he kissed my intensely.

'I love you, Charlie; I'm going to make you so happy.'

I felt myself filling with tears; this was the first time somebody had said this to me, and I knew he meant it. This was the happiest I had felt. The rape incident had got me down, and I wasn't sure I would ever trust a man, but Sebastian made me feel different. I chose not to tell Sebastian about the rape incident. There was no need for him to know what had happened. I didn't want him to feel more pressured about sex and what I had been through.

'I love you too, Sebastian.'

He looked at me and smiled.

'I'm so glad you said that, Charlie. I hoped you felt the same way.'

It had started to snow outside.

'Look, Charlie, at the snowflakes falling.'

'Wow, this is magical, Sebastian.'

We jumped out of bed to the window looking out; it was magical. I felt like my fairy godmother had answered all my prayers. Sebastian put his arms around me.

'I never asked, Charlie, are you on the pill? We haven't used anything, and I wouldn't want you to get pregnant and ruin your education. We have to do things the right way.'

'It's okay, Sebastian. I'm on the pill.'

We kissed and snogged and ended back in the bed having sex again. It didn't hurt as much as the first time; I think he had broken me in. This was the best Christmas ever; we never got up and had sex a third time in the afternoon to 'Rocking around the Christmas Tree' by Brenda Lee, and the third time we rocked the bed. We got better each time.

From then on, we were an official item together and full-on dating. We introduced each other to our families. We were joined at the hip; we met up before college, during lunch breaks, and after college. We did so much together, theatres, cinema's, meals out and night clubs. We were inseparable and so in love; we adored each other.

Sebastian changed my life and my thinking on men. He got me flowers most weeks and loved to please me. Sebastian would always open the doors for me and be a proper gentleman.

'Ladies first,' he would say.

Sex was intermate. He always made me feel loved and told me how much he loved me. Life couldn't have been better.

The following Christmas, Sebastian proposed to me.

He got down on one knee on Christmas Day. 'Charlie, will you marry me?'

He opened a ring box, and to my surprise, it was an engagement ring I had said I liked. It was a stunning white gold solitaire ring with a single brilliant-cut diamond stone centrepiece adorned with further beautiful round diamonds. It sparkled and glittered against the light.

'Yes, I will, yes, I will marry you, Sebastian.' He slowly put the ring on my finger.

Sebastian kissed me. 'I'm going to make you a very happy wife, Charlie. I will always look after you.'

I was thrilled; it was the next step for us. We wanted children together, and I knew Sebastian would make a great dad.

We set a date for June 1991 to give us time to get a job and save.

CHAPTER 5
MARRYING SEBASTIAN

Sebastian and I both finished college in Summer 1989; it had been a fantastic experience, and we had thoroughly enjoyed our two years at college, spending time together each day. We passed our courses with good grades, which put us in good stead for the future.

It was now our time to move into the real adult world and get a job. We had a wedding planned for June 1991 and needed to save hard. I got a job as a finance trainee in a local office in West Bromwich. The firm I worked for was a cardboard box manufacturing business; they manufactured boxes for large companies such as Swish. I'll always remember the business; they were called 'The Box Company.' I didn't earn a lot as a trainee, only £80 a week, but that was sufficient at the time. One thing they were keen on was for me to continue with my studies. This meant I had to go back to college and study in the evenings. I enrolled for the AAT (Association of Accounting Technicians) in September 1989 and started studying two evenings a week at college. Work and study took its toll a bit. I worked full time, studied two nights until 9.00 pm, and had course work to do the weekends. I didn't get to see as much of Sebastian as much as we would have liked, but we could see the long-term benefits. Sebastian and I were still madly in love with each other, looking forward to our wedding.

Sebastian got a job in a school as a sports assistant teacher. He loved the job; it was right up his street. He got to do all the sport he loved with younger children, in particular football, he enjoyed football. He played a lot of football at weekends while I studied. He became coach of an under

12's football team, which kept him busy. Sebastian earnt slightly more than me, £90 a week, which was good.

We both still lived at home, so we were able to save almost everything we earnt. We opened a joint bank account and put £50 each in a month to save for the wedding. I would stay at Sebastian's house most of the time; there was more room at his house. He was the only child and lived with his mother. His father had left for another women when he was young, and Sebastian never had anything to do with his dad. His mom was charming and kind, very attractive, and enjoyed going out to theatres and cinema's. She was tall and slim like Sebastian; funny though, she had blonde hair and Sebastian was dark, maybe it was coloured, or his father was dark?

My mother's health had deteriorated, and my father had now given up his job to care for her. She was wheelchair bound, which made it difficult to get around the small council house. The council put rails around the house and a ramp outside to try to help with her mobility.

The sex was still good between Sebastian and I; we would have sex whenever we got chance when his mom was out. It was as good as the first time, but we were far more experienced then that time and explored a bit more. I still never talked about my rape experience; I didn't want to spoil what we had. I don't know why I thought he would see me differently, I just did. Every week, Sebastian bought me flowers. He was so sweet and adorable.

On one occasion, Sebastian and I had been out night clubbing with some old friends from college. We had not been out clubbing for a long time as we were too busy saving. We arrived back at Sebastian's house around 2.00 am very drunk. I wore a short tight shift dress with fishnet stockings and high heels. I knew Sebastian was desperate to get me to bed, but his mom was home in bed. We started kissing in the lounge, and he started moving his hands up and down my stockings.

'Charlie, I need to make love to you. I love you in stockings, you look sexy.'

'We can't, babe, your mom's in bed and will hear us.'

'We'll stay downstairs, Charlie.'

'What if you mom comes down?'

'I'll take the blame.' He laughed

He pushed me down onto the sofa. We started snogging, giggling like naughty kids doing something we shouldn't be doing. Sebastian stood and dropped his trousers and boxers; his penis was already hard. He lay on top of me on the sofa and lifted my dress up feeling his way around my stockings.

'You know how to turn me on, Charlie.'

I laughed, 'Oh, yes, I know exactly how to seduce you, Sebastian.'

He pulled off my pants and pushed his penis inside me. We didn't bother with any foreplay; I was wet, and Sebastian was hard, and we were too drunk to be intermate. We just wanted hard sex. We started to make loud noises as the sex got faster and harder.

'God, Charlie, I'm coming.'

'Ahhh, Sebastian, come with me.'

After it was all over, we both quickly got dressed and sneaked quietly upstairs to bed.

I giggled. 'Do you think your mom heard?'

'No, she'll be fast asleep at this time. Anyway, if she did, I'll say you screamed because you saw a spider.'

Sebastian knew I had a phobia about spiders.

'I didn't scream.'

He held my hand. 'Yes, you did. I always make you scream.'

We laughed and giggled again.

The next morning, we got up with sore heads; it was about 11.00 am when we got up, very late for us. Sebastian's mom was in the garden doing some gardening. She popped her head round the patio door

'Morning both, you both look at bit for wear. Did you have a good night?'

I let Sebastian answer. 'Yes, Mom, we had a really good night.'

'Oh, good. I know it was late when you back, about 2.00 am, I think.'

My heart sank; she was awake. I looked at Sebastian, and he smiled and shouted back

'Something like that, Mom, don't know exactly what time it was.'

She carried on gardening and shouted, 'It was about 2.00 am, Sebastian. You woke me up. There was a lot of noise going on downstairs. Goodness knows what you were both up to?'

This was so embarrassing; she must have heard us.

'There was a spider, Mom. You know what Charlie is like. I'd had a few drinks, so you can imagine me trying to capture it to put it outside.'

I took a deep breath. I could not believe what Sebastian had just said. He looked at me and winked, putting his finger to my mouth. 'Shhhhh.'

It was silent for a minute, then his mom said, 'Must have been a big spider, took you a while to catch it.'

We both started to giggle; she must have heard us; this was so embarrassing. Whoever wants their parents to hear them having sex?

After that episode, we decided to find somewhere to live. We rented a small terraced house in West Bromwich that would do us for a short time. We made it homely with candles, cushions, and photos. It was nice to have our own place. We could do what we like, when we liked. Sebastian continued to buy me flowers every week; they smelt beautiful in the house.

The wedding was getting closer and closer. We had booked a small church in Dudley, St Mary's, then a party after in the church a hall with a disco and food. We had started saving for a mortgage, so we didn't want to spend too much on the wedding.

Our wedding day was Saturday 22nd June 1991. My parents couldn't afford to pay anything towards the wedding; they could barely afford to live themselves, and I wouldn't have expected them to. We had worked out the cost of the wedding, and we knew the cost of the church service, food and drinks, flowers, and the cars. Sebastian agreed that they would hire suits for him, the best man, and my dad. We agreed to have ivory suits with purple cravats, and I agreed to have an ivory dress to match; all was sorted and within our budget. The only thing left was my dress. I was a bit lapse and hadn't really looked and chose one.

Sebastian insisted, 'Charlie, I want you to have whatever dress you want; don't worry about the cost. I want you to look and feel like a princess on the day.'

I was conscious about the cost; we had a tight budget, and I wanted to keep within that budget. I shopped around until I found the most magnificent dress. It was in a charity shop in town. It was an ivory silhouette ballgown type of dress with a fitted lace bodice at the top, the neckline was a V-neck shape showing off the bust. It was the perfect fairy tale wedding dress. I tried it on, it fit perfect.

Sebastian was aghast that I had purchased my dress from a charity shop. I was used to having second-hand clothes as a child from jumble sales; it didn't bother me. I loved the dress, and I felt a princess in it.

'Charlie, you can have any dress you like. You don't have to go to a charity shop.'

'I love it, Sebastian. I feel like a princess in it, I don't think I could find anything as nice in a shop. It's designer as well.'

Sebastian smiled and kissed me on the head. 'As long as you're happy, Charlie.'

The big day was here before we knew it. The weather was glorious. My dad cried when he saw me in my dress. I had my hair clipped in curls and wore a princess tiara; I didn't want a veil.

'Charlie, you look so beautiful and elegant. You look like a princess; Sebastian is one hell of a lucky man to have you.'

My mother manged to get to the wedding along with my younger brother and elder sister. The day was simple but fantastic.

My dad walked me down the aisle. Sebastian looked at me up and down as I arrived at his side; he held my hand

'Charlie, you look beautiful, like a fairy tale princess, I love you so much and will always look after you.'

I will always remember those words; they meant so much to me. The ceremony started, and it was soon time to take our wedding vows. We were nervous about this bit in case we messed up, and it made us giggle when we were practicing. I was glad Sebastian went first. We turned to each and held hands; Sebastian looked straight into my eyes.

'I, Sebastian Edward Dyson, take you, Charlotte Louise Bennett
to be my wife,
to have and to hold
from this day forward;
for better, for worse,
for richer, for poorer,
in sickness and in health,
to love and to cherish,
till death us do part,
according to God's holy law.
In the presence of God I make this vow.'

I had a nervous laugh, but now it was my turn. I prayed I didn't get it wrong.

'I, Charlotte Louise Bennett, take you, Sebastian Edward Dyson
to be my husband,
to have and to hold
from this day forward;
for better, for worse,
for richer, for poorer,
in sickness and in health,
to love and to cherish,
till death us do part,
according to God's holy law.
In the presence of God I make this vow.'

Then, it was the exchange of the rings. We had chosen matching white gold bands with diamonds set into the bands. Sebastian's was a much wider band than mine.

Sebastian put the ring on my finger saying, 'I give you this ring as a sign of my faithful devotion. I will always love you, cherish you, and honour the vows spoken here today.'

I repeated the same words and put the ring on Sebastian's finger.

The priest then pronounced us man and wife and said, 'You may now kiss the bride.'

Sebastian, being so tall and muscular, lifted me off the floor and gave me a big sloppy kiss. It was so funny; he didn't want to put me down; my lipstick was all over my face.

We were both looking forward to our wedding day but very nervous about the ceremony, in truth, we were both glad when the ceremony was over. The rest of day was beautiful. We had photographs in the beautifully designed church gardens, then partied the day and night away. We had the first dance to 'Perfect Day' by Lou Reed, the first song we danced to the night Sebastian told me he loved me.

Sebastian had a wonderful surprise for me on the evening. I thought we were going back home to our council house, but he had booked a wedding suite at a local hotel. Sebastian was so thoughtful and loved surprising me. The bridal room was magnificent; it had a huge four poster bed, tea and coffee facilities, and a beautiful tiled en-suite. We felt like royalty. I had never stayed in a place like this before. Sebastian bounced on the bed and lay back; he looked so handsome in his wedding suite. I had never seen him in suite before, he only ever wore sportswear or jeans.

He sat up. 'Come here, Mrs Dyson,' and he pulled me towards him 'You look absolutely gorgeous in that dress, a princess, my princess.'

Sebastian sat on the edge of the bed, and I stood in between his legs as we kissed.

'Do you want me to undo your dress for you, Mrs Dyson?'

'I think you should, Mr Dyson. I can't manage it on my own.'

I turned around and he undone the hooks and zip on my dress. It dropped to the floor, and I stepped out of it, placing it carefully on the chair. Underneath the dress I wore a lacey bask with a matching thong, ivory stockings, and a garter.

'Oh my god, Charlie, you look a million dollars. I am the luckiest man ever to marry you.'

'You are, Mr Dyson; remember your vows you have to look after me now till death do us part.'

He pulled me towards him, 'Always, Charlie. I'll never let you go.'

We made love most of the night, three times to be precise; it was not dirty sex but very intermate, telling each other how much we loved each other. The perfect wedding night.

Our lives had just begun as a married couple. I became Mrs Charlotte Louise Dyson. Sebastian enjoyed calling me Mrs Dyson from time to time; he liked the thought that I was now officially his wife.

CHAPTER 6
SEBASTIAN'S CHILDREN

Over the next few years, we carried on much of a muchness. I finished my exams with top grades, which allowed me to move on to a better job with a higher salary. Sebastian worked his way up the ladder to be a teacher from an assistant still teaching sport.

We found a house to buy, which was perfect for us; it was a semi-detached in Bromsgrove on the outskirts of Birmingham. We had managed to save just enough money for the deposit. We moved into the house in January 1993. It had three bedrooms and a huge garden. It needed modernising a bit, but I was confident Sebastian could do that over time.

'Big garden, Charlie, all we need now is kids.'

I hadn't told Sebastian, but I stopped the contraceptive pill three months earlier. I worked it out so that I was entitled to maternity pay from my new job.

We worked on the house over the next few months, painting and decorating. We ordered new carpets and made it homely. It April 1993, I missed my period. I had butterflies when I told Sebastian.

'Sebastian, I've missed my period.'

'What? I didn't know we were trying?'

'I stopped the pill a few months back, and now I've missed a period.'

'Charlie, that would be great. Have you done a test?'

'No, babe, I'm only a few days late.'

'Let's get one and see. I need to know; this would be great, Charlie.'

We went out and got a test from the chemist. The next morning, we both awoke early, excited that I was going to do the test.

'Go on, Charlie, do the test.'

I got out of bed and went to the bathroom. I sat on the toilet and pee'd on the stick. I left it a minute, then looked, the blue line appeared on the result, which meant I was pregnant.

I froze with excitement. Sebastian was impatient to get the result; he came to the bathroom door.

'Charlie, what's the result?'

I opened the door and stared at him for a few seconds. 'I'm pregnant, Sebastian, you're going to be a dad.'

He picked me up and swung me round.

'Oh my god, Charlie. I can't believe it; that's the best news ever.'

We were ecstatic with the news, life was good, it was like Christmas. I had it confirmed at the doctors, and Sebastian and I started to plan the new addition soon to come into our lives. My due date was 15th December 1993. Sebastian would not let me do anything; he wouldn't let me carry shopping, hoover, or stress out about anything. He was the perfect gentlemen who adored and cared for his wife and future child. At three months pregnant, we went for the first scan, and we could see the baby very clearly. He held my hand tightly, rubbing it while the scan was being done.

'Can you tell if it's a boy or girl?' he asked.

The nurse looked further. 'I'm sorry, no; we can't be sure at this stage. I can't get a clear view the way the baby is lying.'

It was fascinating to see the baby on the screen. Sebastian and I got a scanned image of the baby to take away with us. We were so happy, and we couldn't wait to bring a child into our lives. We hardly had sex since Sebastian knew I was so pregnant; he was very protective, and for some reason, thought it might hurt the baby. I laughed and went along with it.

It was about two weeks after my scan, I hadn't felt too well. I had stomach cramps and felt fatigued. I called the doctor, and he said it was probably my hormones changing and to get plenty of rest. I awoke in the night with a sudden wet feeling and stomach cramps. I pulled the sheet off me to see blood everywhere. I shook Sebastian to wake him.

'Sebastian, Sebastian, I don't know what's happening.'

He looked at me.

'Oh my god, Charlie. I'll call the hospital right away, don't move.'

He jumped out of bed, put his sleep shorts on, and went downstairs to phone the hospital.

I had the most horrific stomach cramps. I got out of bed holding my stomach and headed for the bathroom. My nightdress was covered in blood, as was the bed. I sat on the toilet, and I lost lots of blood clots. What an earth was happening? I thought.

Sebastian came running back upstairs all a fluster.

'We have to go to the hospital now, Charlie.'

He helped me change into something fresh. I put a pad on and took towels with me to sit on in the car. Tears rolled down my face.

'It's going to be okay, Charlie.'

Somehow, I didn't think so.

We got to the hospital, and I was rushed through even before Sebastian had checked me in. They did a scan, then a consultant came in to examine me. Afterwards, he sat on the end of the bed and gave us the bad news.

'I'm sorry, Mr and Mrs Dyson, but you have had a miscarriage.'

'Are you sure?' Sebastian asked.

'Yes, Mr Dyson, this is very common in the early stages of pregnancy.'

My eyes filled with tears; I knew deep down before we got there. Sebastian's eyes filled up with water. He put his arms around me and held me tightly.

'It's okay, babe, we have each other; we'll get through this.' Sebastian was always the stronger one at times like this.

When we got home, the bed required stripping and cleaning. I looked at it and burst into tears.

'That was our baby, Sebastian.'

He got me to sit downstairs with a cup of tea while he cleaned the bed; he didn't want me to go back into the bedroom and be upset. That night, we slept in the spare bedroom. Sebastian held me tight and comforted me. He kept strong even though he was hurting too.

I didn't ever come to terms with the miscarriage, but some of the pain and hurt healed with time. Sebastian and I didn't have sex for a good couple of months after. I lost interest and was scared in case it happened again. Sebastian as usual, was a gentleman, he understood and didn't push me for sex; he comforted me and held me tight when I cried.

The remining months of 1993 held its own; we both worked hard. I still thought of the miscarriage every day. We had sex again for the first time in the September on my birthday. I'd had a few drinks and let myself go a bit.

December was the hardest month. I thought about our child being born if I hadn't miscarried and our first Christmas with a child. I was still grieving. Sebastian supported me as much as he could.

After Christmas, Sebastian and I went out for a meal; it was his birthday January 15th. He held my hand.

'Charlie, I know it was a hard year last year. Let's try for another baby, babe.'

'I don't know, Sebastian, what if it happens again, what if it's me? I couldn't face all that again.'

'We have to move on, Charlie; you can't live in the past. I love you so much, and we have so much to look forward to.'

Sebastian held my hands and squeezed them. 'What do you say?'

He pinched my chin. 'We have to move on, babe.'

I knew he was right, but I found it hard to let go. It was time to try, he was right.

I came off the pill at the end of January and our sex life got back on track; we had fun in the bedroom like we used to have. Sebastian would regularly bring me breakfast in bed on a Sunday in the nude; it was funny to watch. He would put a red rose in his mouth and walk in with a tray for me. He spoilt me rotten.

We got to April. The buds were coming up on the flowers in the garden. I thought back to finding out I was pregnant the year before, and I wondered what our lives would be like with a baby.

May was a special month. I missed my period at the beginning of the month. I had been reflecting a lot about the year before and couldn't believe this could be happening again. I left it a few days to be sure, then told Sebastian.

Soon after, one morning in bed I told him, 'Sebastian, I'm late with my period.'

He jumped up with excitement. 'How late?'

'Five days now.'

'Oh my gosh, Charlie, why didn't you tell me sooner? We'll have to get a test.'

'I've got one.'

I pulled it out of my bedside cabinet.

'You little gem, go do it, go on, Charlie.'

This was a bit of Déjà vu; I was so nervous my hand was shaking.

'Do you want me to come with you to the bathroom?'

I nodded, 'Yes, is that okay?'

Sebastian put his arms around me and held me tight, 'Of course, it is.'

We threw off the covers and went into the bathroom. I unwrapped the test and sat on the toilet. Sebastian sat on the side looking away but chatting to me all the time, something about football, I think. I pee'd on the test and held it in my hand. Sebastian was still mumbling on about football. I looked at the test and the line came up immediately

'Sebastian, I'm pregnant.'

He jumped off the side and looked at the test. I was still sitting on the toilet; he knelt in front of me and held one hand at each side of my face

'Charlie, babe, this is the best news ever; we will be okay. It's meant to be.'

He hugged me tightly, then let go.

He laughed. 'I'd better let you get off the toilet.'

The first few months were hard. I felt mixed emotions ranging from cautiously optimistic one day to overwhelmingly anxious the next. I felt on high alert, trying to detect any possible symptoms of miscarriage. Being pregnant again did comfort me, ease the feelings of loss, but at the same time, I felt guilty and worried about forgetting my last pregnancy.

The time came for the scan, we both went along as before. Sebastian and I filled up with so emotion when we saw the baby on the scan; it looked perfect as before.

'Can you tell the sex?' I asked

The nurse looked closer and smiled. 'I would say that it's a boy.'

Sebastian and I looked at each other. Oh my gosh, a boy; it was unbelievable. My due date was the 9th of January 1995.

We went home, full of emotional happiness after the scan; the picture was beautiful, a little baby boy.

'I hope we're okay this time, Sebastian.'

He hugged and kissed me on the head.

'It will be, Charlie, trust me.'

The next few weeks, I panicked about every cramp. I hardly slept. I held my stomach in bed at night and prayed that I didn't miscarry like before. Sebastian and I banned sex from the minute I found out I was pregnant. Sebastian was fine with this. We wanted to give this baby every chance. As the weeks went by, my tummy grew into a bump, and I started to feel movement. Most nights, Sebastian would lie and put his hand on my tummy to feel the baby move; he was fascinated by it.

I refused to do the nursery or buy baby clothes until my next scan, which was scheduled for twenty-one weeks. We got to the twenty-one-week scan, we both cried when we saw the baby on the scan, and they said everything was well.

This was it now; it was time to kit the nursery out. Sebastian worked so hard and decorated the room in Winnie the Pooh. We went shopping together to Mothercare and chose the cot and the pram.

Christmas this year was special compared to last year, albeit I still didn't forget the baby we had lost, this baby helped me to overcome the grief. Sebastian and I would put our hands on my tummy and watch the kicks.

'He's going to be a footballer like you.'

'That's my boy, Charlie.'

I went into labour on the 4th of January in the evening. Sebastian went to bed around 10.30 am as he had work the next day. I felt a bit niggly so sat up a bit longer. I was also uncomfortable in bed as I was so big. The niggly pain got worse and around 11.30 pm contractions started. I woke Sebastian.

'Sebastian, I think I'm in labour.'

He jumped out of bed. 'Are you sure'?

'Yes, the pains are coming regularly, and it's really hurting.'

He called the hospital to inform them, and they said tell her to take her time, have a hot bath then see how the pains are. When the contractions are more regular, about every twenty minutes, bring your wife into hospital.

Sebastian ran me a hot bath. I carefully got in and lay for a while, but the contractions were still coming strong and fast. Sebastian helped me out the bath and into a robe.

I walked into the lounge and had the biggest contraction ever. I bent over, holding the fireplace, crying out. Then suddenly, there was a gush on the floor; my water had broken.

'Sebastian, this baby is coming, I can feel it, I'm in agony.'

Sebastian called the hospital back, and they said bring her in immediately.

I don't know how I got in the car. I could hardly walk; the pain was crucifying. Sebastian drove through red lights to get me to the hospital. I had my legs up on the dash on the car and screamed out, I was in so much pain.

On arrival at the hospital, a porter greeted us with a wheelchair. I couldn't even stand by this stage. He wheeled me to the maternity ward, where they lay me on the bed. I always remember a gynaecology consultant coming to give me an internal, it hurt so much with the contractions, I kicked out.

'Just f'cking leave me alone.'

The consultant sat on the side of the bed.

'Mrs Dyson, your baby is breeched and trying to come out feet first. I've just tried to turn the baby but without success. Your water has broken, so we don't have time to waste; we need to take you to theatre to do a caesarean.'

I looked at Sabastian, as I doubled up in pain from the next contraction.

'Please, just stop the pain,' I shouted.

Sebastian nodded to the doctor. 'Let's go to theatre, Charlie.'

I nodded.

'Okay, we'll get Charlie ready for theatre.'

Before I knew it, they injected into the bottom of my back, which took all the pain away in minutes. I couldn't feel my legs. They gave me a form to sign. I didn't even read it. I scribbled my name. They took my nail varnish off and shaved my vaginal area. A theatre nurse came to me.

'Mrs Dyson, you are ready for theatre.'

'Is Sebastian coming with me?' I asked

'Yes, Mrs Dyson, we are going to get him prepared to meet you in the theatre.'

He held my hand tightly. 'I'm with you, Charlie, all the way.'

I held Sebastian's hand tightly.

'Please, don't leave me.'

'I won't, babe; we are going through this together.'

The hospital staff pushed my bed down to theatre; the doctor entered all dressed in a theatre gown on and a hat. Sebastian shortly followed dressed in a gown and what looked like wellies; he stood at the side of me and held my hand. A screen was put over my tummy. I guess it was so I could not see anything. The radio was on in the background, bit strange I thought to have music in a theatre, but it did help to relax me.

The doctor looked over the screen. 'Right, Mrs Dyson, tell me if can feel anything.'

I didn't know what he was doing, but I couldn't feel anything.

'Did you feel that?'

'No, Doctor, I can't feel anything.'

'Okay, good; we'll start.'

It was a strange feeling during the operation. I felt some tugging in my abdomen area. I knew someone was inside me pulling and tugging, but it didn't hurt. Not sure how long it went on for, it seemed ages, but I don't think it was.

'Okay, Mrs Dyson, we are now lifting the baby out; you have a wonderful little boy.'

I saw a nurse carry the baby over to the side, then I heard a baby's cry. Sebastian and I looked at each other with joy. The nurse wrapped our baby in a blanket and handed him over to me.

'Here's your son, Mr and Mrs Dyson, he was born at six minutes past three, weighing seven pounds, two ounces.'

I held him in my arms. He looked so tiny; he had Sebastian's big blue eyes and a mop of dark hair like Sebastian. Sebastian kissed us.

'I love you, Charlie, and you little Mitch.' A few tears ran down his face as he said it.

The doctor looked over.

'Okay, Mrs Dyson, a few more things to do to remove the placenta and stitch you up, then we're all done here.'

I smiled back at him; I didn't really care what they did to me now that little Mitch was safe.

So, our first baby, Mitch Joseph Dyson was born at 3.06 am on the 5th of January 1995. The next two years were full of joy; we were doting parents. We treasured every moment, the first step, the first tooth, the first word, which was Dad!

Mitch was just three and starting nursery when I found out I was pregnant again. I didn't tell Sebastian this time until after I'd done the test. He was thrilled, we always said we didn't want Mitch to be a lonely child.

'Only two though,' Sebastian would say. He always thought two children was the ideal family.

I felt much more tired with this pregnancy; it was hard running around after a three-year-old and juggling work too. I also had dreadful nausea in a morning from an early stage. I never had this with Mitch. This pregnancy was very different to the first. I lost weight in the beginning because I had nausea so bad.

Everything went well with the three-month scan; the baby was healthy.

Sebastian was very supportive; he would take Mitch out to the park to give me a rest, and he did a lot of the cooking and cleaning. He would not let me carry any shopping, not even a bag with a few items in it, just as it was with the first. The baby was very active from about twenty-four weeks, often keeping me up at night. I would lie by Sebastian at night on the sofa once we had got Mitch to bed. Sebastian would put his hand on my tummy and feel the baby kicking around.

It was time for our twenty-six-week scan. The nurse put the jelly on my belly and started the scan, clicking on computer every few minutes.

'The baby is fine; all the measurements are good. Do you want to know what sex it is?'

Sebastian and I hadn't talked about this. We looked at each other, I nodded, and he smiled back at me.

He held my hand saying to the nurse, 'Yes, we would.'

'It's a baby girl.'

Whatever the gender, we would have loved our baby, but the news of a girl was wonderful news. That evening, we spoke to Mitch with excitement.

'You have a little sister coming, you'll have to look after your little sister.'

Sebastian and I were thrilled, we went through a lot of girl's names, finally we came up with the name Summer. It felt different and unique, special for our little girl. I got the name from hearing about an American model on TV, Summer Altice; she had won a magazine cover girl contest in 1995.

Towards the end of the pregnancy, the doctors informed me that it would be best to have a caesarean again to reduce the risk of any ruptures to my previous scar. Sebastian and I agreed and set a date for the birth; it felt strange this time, knowing the actual date Summer would be born.

Summer was born on the 16th of April 1999 at 11.06 am, she weighed six pounds and two ounces.

Like Mitch, she had big blue eyes and a mop of dark curly hair.

We were now the perfect family, a happy marriage and two wonderful children, just as we had planned.

Sebastian and I would always make time for each other away from the kids. We had regular date nights on our own, we knew a happy marriage was making time for each other and maintaining a healthy sex life. It was important to us.

CHAPTER 7
GROWING MIDDLE AGED TOGETHER

Sadly, my mother passed away not long after Summer was born, and my father passed away six months later. I think he had broken heart syndrome; he had cared for my mom for many years, and they were so devoted and in love. I was so pleased that they got to see me get married and have kids. They loved their grandchildren; they bought so much joy into their lives.

I missed my parents; it left a big gap in my life. Most weekends, I would visit them and take the children. Summer was still a baby, but Mitch was very inquisitive and talkative. Mitch loved to get in my mother's wheelchair or mess with her with her walker. I'd often think back to when I was a young child out playing, with Jason always up to no good, happy memories.

Sebastian's mother babysat a lot for Mitch and Summer whilst we went out on our date nights. Life was good and the sex continued; the children would stay over with their nanny whilst we went out and partied or sometimes had a nice romantic meal. We would always make the best of the night and finish off in bed having intimate sex. I loved to dress up for Sebastian, knowing this would turn him on even more.

Sebastian's mother sadly got cancer when the kids were early teens. We supported and aided her for months. Unfortunately, the breast cancer spread. She fought hard, but sadly lost her life to the dreadful disease. As a family, we were all upset and grieved; it is sad to see anyone suffer.

We had good memories of our family, losing them so young made us realise you must live life to the full and live for today.

This changed our lives and our marriage. We no longer had a babysitter on call; in fact, we had no babysitter at all. All though the children were reaching their teens, we were uncomfortable leaving them on their own for longer than a couple of hours, and even then, we relied on Mitch to look after Summer as she was four years younger.

This was when our marriage seemed to come into difficulty. We spent less time together on our own, and sex was infrequent. Sebastian began a new job as a personal trainer. He said it would allow him more time to spend with the family. In fact, this was the opposite. He worked more and more weekends and evenings, which was the time we would spend together as a family.

I cooked most nights and evenings for the family, but Sebastian's meal would generally go in the oven cold waiting for him to come home from work. I appeared to pick up the pressure of two teenage kids with no outlet and working full-time. Sexually, we would be lucky to have sex on a Saturday or Sunday morning, pending how tired we were.

Then, one Sunday, my heart was shattered. Mobiles and social media were becoming a thing of the future, fatal for a marriage breakdown. I got Sebastian a new mobile for his birthday, and he joined on Facebook, a social networking site. Sebastian explained it was a way to connect with new clients and old friends. I always trusted Sebastian, so I had no reason to doubt what he told me.

That night, Sebastian was fast asleep in bed, and his mobile kept bleeping. I was so curious, not that I didn't trust him, but the curiosity got the better of me. I got out of bed, and sneakily picked up his mobile and took it downstairs with me. I made myself a hot cup of tea and sat on the sofa with Sebastian's mobile. I took a deep breath thinking 'Should I really be doing this? Is Sebastian cheating on me? Our sex life hasn't been as good, is there another woman?'

I pressed on the button on the phone to activate it, and it prompted for a password. I punched Mitches date of birth into the phone but no joy, then Summers and then mine, no joy with either. My mind was in overdrive. What was the password? I then punched in Sebastian's mother's date of birth. Bingo, I was in. Sebastian always used dates of births for passwords. My heart started beating so fast, I couldn't believe

I was doing this. Sebastian and I had always been so close, how could I doubt him? I was so scared of what I might see or read.

I clicked onto Facebook first and looked at Sebastian's friends. There appeared to be a lot of friends from school, in particular women. Sebastian had never really discussed his school days or any previous girlfriends before me. I looked in Sebastian's Facebook messages and there was one woman by the name of 'Angie' who appeared. Immediately, I became insecure, hurt, and jealous. The thought of Sebastian chatting to other women from his past and not mentioning it to me didn't feel right.

I clicked on the messages:

'Great to connect with you, Sebastian, bet you are as hot as at school xx.'

'Still keep myself fit, Ang, what you up to these days?'

'Single mom with a child but doing okay. How about you? Xx.'

'Yea, I'm doing okay. You know me, still into the gym. Working as a personal trainer.'

'I need a personal trainer, Sebastian; bet you could get me in shape? Xx.'

'Lol, I'm sure I could.'

'I miss the good old days, Sebastian; we had some fun together. Xx.'

'Yep, I remember the days over the fields, we had a lot of fun, Ang.'

'Do you remember the first day you kissed me? Oh my god, we were so young. Xx.'

'Yea, I remember that first kiss, how could I not forget'?

'God, Sebastian, I remember us snogging and you put your hands down my pants. That was the first time I'd ever felt squeamish. Xx.'

'The good old days, Ang.'

'Yep, the good old days; we could have been together now if you hadn't dumped me for Sarah.'

My god, I felt sick at what I'd read, and who the hell was Sarah? Sebastian and I were supposed be virgin lovers, sex for the first time, love at first sight, had we lived a lie all through our relationship?

I searched for Sarah in Sebastian's phone to see what came up.

Sarah Jackson, this was the name that popped up on Sebastian's Facebook. Again, I started to read the messages. I started from the last message upwards.

'You loved me, Sarah, lol. I loved me too, just wasn't meant to be.'

My heart sank, and I felt sick. I never expected anything at all like this from Sebastian. I was his first love, I had his children, and I thought he worshipped me. May be this was why our sex life had deteriorated? I thought.

I had no choice but to read back on the messages.

'I think Ang got jealous when we got together; remember us holding hands and kissing at high school.'

'I do, Sarah. Ang was many months before you and we were very young.'

'It was a shame we lost contact when you went to college. You never answered my messages.'

'Sorry, Sarah. I kept meaning to call you. College and studying took over my life, and as time went on, it was more difficult to contact you.'

'What are you up to these days, Sarah?'

'Not a lot, Sebastian. I had Richard my son at the age of sixteen, so never got into a permanent relationship. Who wants to be with a single mother at that age? I've been with a few men as I've got older but nothing serious.'

'You had a son that young?'

'Yes, we kept it low key within the family. Sebastian, are you panicking it's your child?'

'Err no, just surprised you had a child so young.'

I felt even more sick and could not ignore this. How could Sebastian be a father so young if he was a virgin, and why would this conversation be happening if that were so. I didn't feel like I knew my husband at all. I had to read on.

'So how about you, Seb, what's happened in your life?'

How dare she call him Seb. I had never done that in all the time I'd known him.

'You know, like you, I moved on and had a couple of kids.'

'Nice, and is there a Mrs Dyson?'

'There had to be a Mrs Dyson to have the kids, Sarah.'

'I like the word "had", better than has, Sebastian, you always kept things secret.'

'No, I don't, we're going back a long time ago, Sarah.'

'Do you go out drinking much, Sebastian?'

'Not really, why?'

'There's a school reunion a week on Saturday at the Wreck Club, why don't you come'?

On that, I locked the mobile. I couldn't read anymore. Tears rolled down my face, emotions filled my body. I had trusted Sebastian, and to read this broke my heart in two. I wasn't sure I knew Sebastian anymore, or if I ever had at all. Not sure what to do, I took the mobile back upstairs and put it back on Sebastian's bedside cabinet. I got back into bed and lay still with tears streaming down on my pillow. Sebastian was snoring with no idea what I had read. I wanted to wake him, but the anger and emotion would have fuelled things and we would have argued and woke Mitch and Summer.

I hardly slept thinking about what I'd read; it was as if someone had ripped my heart out, the feeling of betrayal. I kept thinking about if the child were Sebastian's all this time and no mention of it, why would she say that if they hadn't had sex? Then I began to think about what I would do if it were true, could I trust him going forward and would it be the end of our marriage? We had always been so devoted to each other and the family, I couldn't get my head around why he would go back to his past and connect with this girl.

I then started to think about Sebastian's mother passing, wondering whether that had played a part in his behaviour to feel a need to talk to someone from the past. Our marriage hadn't been brilliant as late, sex wasn't brilliant, maybe Sebastian was looking for an affair. Perhaps our marriage was more broken than I ever imagined. Lots of questions went through my mind, even to a point of blaming myself and wondering if I had pushed him away.

My next thoughts were what to do next. Should I confront him? Should I message Sarah? I lay in bed pondering my next steps. In the end, I decided to keep quiet about what I'd learned. I decided so see if Sebastian mentioned the reunion on the following Saturday or if he asked to go out or deliberately be out.

That week, I watched his every movement, every call, and every message he made on his phone. It was a good job I was at work to keep myself sane, the pain was hurting, and I cried every moment I was alone. Sebastian carried on as normal with the gym and his training, oblivious to anything I had read. He left his mobile lying around if he went for a shower or to do other things, but he had no idea I knew the password. I kept the secret to myself and didn't discuss it with anyone. I felt completely isolated.

Thursday evening was the catalyst where everything blew up. Sebastian was home early, and the kids were out at friends. He entered the kitchen and grabbed a beer, chatting to me whilst I was cooking dinner,

'There's a school reunion Saturday night at the Wreck. I might pop there for an hour to see an old friend if that's okay with you.'

My whole body froze, and my hands started to shake; this was the moment I didn't want to happen. I kept my back to Sebastian facing the cooker so that he couldn't see my face or hands

'Oh, you've not mentioned it before. Where did you hear about that?'

'From some old friends, didn't know about it till recently.'

'I might come with you; we haven't been out together for ages.'

'Charlie, we don't have a babysitter. I'll only be a few hours max.'

'The kids will be okay for a few hours, Sebastian, they're old enough.'

'Mitch is staying over at his friends, Charlie, remember he asked. I don't think Summer should be left alone'.

I could feel my eyes filling with water, struggling to hold it in anymore. I turned around, and said, 'Sebastian, who's Sarah?'

'Sarah, Sarah who?'

'The girl you've been messaging on your phone.'

Sebastian's face turned red 'It's a girl I knew from school, she sent me a friend request and I accepted it.'

The tears rolled down my face. 'Sebastian, I know, I've read the messages; don't take me for a fool.'

By this point, I was sobbing. 'Is it an affair? Is that why you want to go to the Wreck?'

Sebastian stood still and stared at me as if he were in shock, 'Charlie, oh my god, you think I'm having an affair'?

He put his arms around me and held me tight, kissing me on the head. I sobbed and sobbed on his shoulder. 'Charlie, I would never do that, I love you.'

As I sobbed, I struggled to breathe; the pain and emotions took over my whole body. I couldn't get a word out of my mouth for the sobbing.

Sebastian could see I was an emotional wreck and struggling to breathe. He guided me slowly, holding my hand into the lounge and sat me down, still holding my hand tightly as I continued to cry

'Charlie, you've got believe me. I haven't done anything.'

I finally held it together to be able to speak, ignoring the denial he was pleading.

'Is it because you have felt neglected or mistreated or not valued? Tell me why.'

'Charlie, I promise you on Summer and Mitches life, I haven't done anything.'

All the feelings of betrayal that come with infidelity surged through my body. He had broken the trust between us, and the feeling of anger came over me. I pushed him off me and stood screaming

'Stop lying, just stop it. I know, I've read the messages.'

He stood to calm me, but I pushed him away. He came back towards me to grab me, but this pushed me into a hysterical state. For that one minute, I lost it, the anger was too much. I grabbed an ornament and threw it at him, just missing his head. The ornament hit the wall and smashed on the floor.

'Charlie, what are you doing? Calm down.'

As Sebastian came towards me for a third time, I punched him so hard in the face, knocking him back. I don't know what got into me, but I went for a second swing at him, he grabbed me putting his arms tight around me to restrain me from hitting out again. I tried to wriggle out, but he was much stronger than me and managed to restrain me down on to the floor. I lay helpless on the floor sobbing whilst Sebastian lay by me still restraining me. He kissed me on the head repeatedly.

'Charlie, please believe me, let's talk like civilised people. I'll do anything to prove to you I haven't done anything wrong. You have to trust me.'

I lay still saying nothing, letting my anger calm down. Sebastian still held me tightly. I felt hopeless lying on the floor. Sebastian slowly let go of me and kissed me on the cheek, wiping my tears away. He kissed me on the lips and begged, 'I love you, Charlie, just give me a chance to explain the messages and the Wreck; it's not what you think. I'll come off Facebook. I'll do anything for you to believe me.'

My heart was thumping. I wanted to believe him and found it hard to believe he would do this and have an affair. I wiped my face and nose with my hands, pulling myself up to a sitting position. I looked a wreck. Sebastian pulled himself up to his knees at the side of me.

'Let's talk, Charlie. I don't want you to think or feel like this; our marriage is too important. Will you listen to me?'

I thought about it for a minute and said nothing. What had I got to lose, I thought, it was out in the open and this was going to go one of two ways? I nodded to Sebastian. He smiled and stood from the floor, offering me a hand to pull myself up.

'Go wash you face, Charlie; I'll make us a nice brew and clean the glass up from the ornament before the kids come back. We'll sit down and talk, even if it takes all night, I don't want to see you like this.'

I went off upstairs to the bathroom and left Sebastian to it. I looked in the mirror at myself. I looked a dreadful mess; my eyes were all red and sore, my face was blotchy from where I'd been crying, my hair was tangled from struggling on the floor, and I looked as if I hadn't slept for a week, probably not far off that. I cleaned myself up and went back downstairs. Sebastian had cleaned the mess up and was sitting on the sofa waiting for me. He tapped the sofa next to him.

'That's my girl; you look much better. Come sit here next to me.'

I sat next to him and hesitantly waited to hear what he had to say.

'Charlie, I have never lied or kept anything from you in all the time of our marriage. I told you I joined Facebook and said I was connecting with old friends, and it would help me attract new work clients. It was Lewis from school who I first connected with, he had connections with a lot of old school friends. It was from that, that a lot of old school friends sent me friend requests. There is absolutely nothing sinister at all. I would have showed you the messages if you'd asked. Yes, a few girls were what you would call girlfriends, but for god sake, Charlie, we were kids. '

'What do you mean by girlfriends?'

'You know we had the odd kiss and mess about as kids do. It's part of growing up and it didn't mean anything.'

'Sarah made a comment that she had a child and some comment about it could be yours.'

'Charlie, she's jesting. I told you when we met, I'd never had sex with anyone else and that is the god's honest truth. There's no way I have children with anyone else; it's impossible. Sarah knows that, which is why she joked saying it.'

'Why didn't you mention Sarah to me when you started messaging each other?'

'It meant nothing, Charlie, nothing at all. I don't want to hear about your boyfriends at school, and I wouldn't expect you to hear anything about mine, they mean nothing.'

'I never had boyfriends at school.'

Sebastian laughed and held my hand. 'C'mon, Charlie; you must have had boyfriends at school and a cheeky kiss, someone as pretty as you.'

I nodded; there was no way I was telling him about my childhood and the rape. Sebastian put his arm around me.

'Aren't I the lucky one then to be the first boyfriend.'

We both paused for a while, then Sebastian got his mobile phone off the table, unlocked it, and went to his messages

'Look, Charlie, you can look at everything. I have nothing to hide.'

'Why did you want to go to the Wreck?'

'It was because Lewis asked me to go, read his messages; it was nothing to do with Sarah telling me about it. I already knew from Lewis and said I would try to pop in. I haven't seen him for ages. Go on have a look. I want you to. There's nothing in there to hide, babe. You'll see I've connected with about twenty old school friends, just friends, that's all they are.'

'Why did you not want me to go to the Wreck with you?'

'Charlie, it wasn't for any particular reason. Please, you're just reading into things. I was only thinking of Summer being on her own; if Mitch was going to be here, then fine. Please read the messages, you've got to believe me.'

I scrolled through some of the messages. Sebastian was right about Lewis asking to meet him at the Wreck for a catch up. Sebastian replied it would only be for an hour if he could make it as we couldn't get babysitters. Sebastian pointed to a message he had wrote to Lewis telling him Sarah had connected with him being flirty, and he joked, 'in her dreams. I love my wife and family dearly; glad I stayed clear of that one.'

'Do you believe me, Charlie? I won't go to the Wreck, and I'll delete Facebook. I'm not bothered about it; you are more important in my life.'

On that, the kids arrived. Sebastian locked his phone and put it on the side.

'What's for dinner, Mom,' they asked walking into the kitchen, Sebastian knew I hadn't finished preparing anything

'I tell you what kids, your mom and I have been busy; if I give you some money will go you and pick up a chippy for us? We'll have a takeaway tonight, your mom's favourite'

Mitch smiled; he loved the chippy same as me. 'Oh yea, Dad, what shall we get?'

'Get fish and chips for your mom, and I and whatever you two want.'

Summer smiled cheekily. 'This is going to cost you, Dad. I'm having the full works.'

Sebastian handed them some money and winked at Summer as they put their shoes back on.

'See, Charlie, we have lovely kids, and I have you. Why would I even risk giving all this up. We always agreed if either of us did anything with anyone else, that would be the end, no going back. I would never risk those consequences.'

Sebastian held my chin and kissed me on the lips, then intimately kissed me. Was he playing me or was this the truth? Everything stacked up what he had said.

'Charlie, can I ask you one thing? Why did you not trust me?'

'Because our marriage hasn't been brilliant, Sebastian. We never do date nights anymore or anything romantic. You hardly tell me you love me, and it's not often we have sex. I'm sorry, but I've felt we are too distanced, and the messages made me think you were having affair. I've felt isolated and alone.'

'I never knew you felt like this, Charlie. Why have you not said anything before?'

'I don't know why. I suppose it's gradually happened over time.'

'Charlie, I'm sorry I've made you feel like this. I didn't realise how insecure you felt. Look, we'll put this right now. I won't go to the Wreck, and I'm going to delete Facebook and get our marriage back on track. I promise I'm going to make time for you. If we can't go out, we'll have a date night at home, and I'll get in the kitchen and cook something up. I hadn't thought of it in the way you had. I assumed everything was okay, but listening to you it isn't, and I want my princess to be happy.'

'Don't get me wrong, Sebastian. We don't argue, but the intimacy between us has gone. All we do is go to work and sleep.'

Sebastian held both my hands tightly. 'I thought it was just us getting older, not that there was a problem. I'm not as energetic these days, Charlie.'

I laughed. 'We're not that old yet.'

'No, we're not; okay, we can do something about this and put it right, starting tonight, let's get the table laid for a family fish and chip super; the kids will be back soon.'

We started to lay the table. Sebastian laughed.

'I can't believe you were jealous of me, Charlie, that's so flattering.'

'I wasn't jealous.'

Sebastian grabbed me and put his arms around my waist. 'You so were.'

He kissed me slowly on the lips. 'I'm going to make love to you tonight. Babe; we have some making up to do.'

On that, the kids arrived back with the food. We all had a fantastic family fish and chip super, and Sebastian kept to his word we made love intimately nearly all night. He deleted Facebook and lost touch with his school friends.

I did believe what he told me, either that or he was very seductive and manipulating. I felt guilty Sebastian deleting his old school friends, but he insisted to prove to me I was the most important thing in his life and not friends from the past.

In the early stages, things improved. We had sex more often, and we made time for each other. It got easier with the kids. Sebastian would help out more, and as they got older, they became more independent, allowing us to have more quality time together.

Of late, we have slipped back into our old ways. We both work hard full-time; the kids have left home, and somehow, we don't find the time for each other. Maybe this is how life is when you're reaching the age of fifty? Sex is infrequent, only when Sebastian feels like it, which is mainly weekends. I feel isolated and alone again. We hardly communicate how we feel. My mood swings change from day to day, and I have no patience with anything. Maybe this is the new norm at our age? Then again, what is the new normal after a coronavirus pandemic and UK lockdown?

PART 2

Life in Lockdown and Menopause

CHAPTER 1
WEEKEND 14TH AND 15TH MARCH 2020

March was an odd month. Everyone started talking about a potential lockdown in the UK and stocking up on supplies. I ignored it all at first and thought this will never happen in the UK. After all, I had a holiday planned in March with my husband Sebastian. We had a holiday planned to Goa on the March 21st, our 19th time to visit Goa.

It was all so unreal when our holiday was cancelled on the 11th of March and told that all the Indian borders were closed due to Covid-19. We had already packed and felt very depressed that our holiday was cancelled. We enjoyed visiting Goa; we had visited so many times that we felt part of the family. Albeit our holiday was cancelled, we didn't unpack. I checked the website daily hoping that the borders would re-open, and we could travel in April 2020.

March 14th was a great day with friends. Friends came over to stay for the weekend, and we drank and ate lots of food. Gemma and John were wonderful friends, we had known them for years. John was a good friend of my husbands; they went back a long way to childhood. It was lovely to see them. We often met up every couple of months, where they would stay at our house.

We still lived in the West Midlands in a nice property, much too big for the two of us since our children left home. We had more room at home than Gemma and John, which is why they always tended to come to us, albeit they lived in a wonderful part of the world in Stratford. We had been there to stay a few times. I loved watching the boats on the river on a summer's day with a prosecco or two!

We enjoyed the weekend with Gemma and John; it was lovely to catch up. Sebastian and John cooked us ladies a wonderful meal whilst we chatted and drank prosecco. Gemma expressed her concerns for Covid-19 as they had a vulnerable disabled son.

'We have stocked up on lots of food in preparation for a lockdown,' Gemma said.

I laughed as I never thought of a lockdown being a serious matter.

Gemma went on to say, 'Charlie, my dear friend, you need to start thinking of lockdown now, it is going to happen and will last a few months.'

I was intrigued by what Gemma had to say. I always thought she was privileged to more information than me. Gemma was rather posh compared to me and spoke very proper. I was from a disadvantaged background and spoke with a rather Black Country accent, not posh at all!

'Charlie darling,' Gemma said, 'look at the news. We are heading for a lockdown in the next few days. We must protect our son, and we have stocked up on lots of dried food, pasta, and toiletries.'

I always found Gemma to be very bright and in the know, so was fascinated to hear her view on the pandemic.

The night passed by very quickly with much more laughing and drinking. I fell asleep on the sofa after a few more drinks; this was usually my party piece when I'd had a few drinks. Sebastian woke me about 11.30 pm.

'C'mon, Charlie it's bedtime; everyone else has gone to bed.'

I was rather dazed and sleepy; however, I pulled myself off the sofa and managed the stairs to bed.

Early the next morning, I awoke at around 6.00 am. This was usual for me during the bright summer months, even on a Saturday or Sunday. I crept downstairs so as not to wake anyone. I went into the kitchen, pleased to see that Sebastian had cleaned all the dishes up from the day before. He usually did the dishes before bed even when he had had a few drinks. There were only a few glasses left to wash. I put the kettle on and washed the glasses whilst waiting for the kettle to boil. I made myself a lovely earl grey tea and moved into the lounge to sit quietly.

I started to hear movement upstairs at around 8.00 am; it was from our bedroom. I knew it was Sebastian going into the bathroom. I made him a cup of tea ready for when he came downstairs. We sat drinking our tea and chatting until Gemma and John arose and appeared downstairs ready for some breakfast. We always cooked a breakfast brunch when visitors stayed over—bacon, eggs, beans the works, just like Sebastian did for me when we first met.

After breakfast, Gemma and John packed up their things ready to leave. It felt different this time to other times. They wished us both well and again talked about the coronavirus pandemic, they left saying 'we hope to see you both on the other side, keep in touch and stay safe.' It still hadn't sunk in with us what was about to occur.

Around lunch time Sebastian started following me around the house, put his arms around my waist.

He kissed my neck. 'Shall we go to bed'?

I gazed at him, knowing that was what he was going to ask; it was a weekend ritual. We were so busy in the week; weekends seemed the only time we got to spend time together sexually these days. We always made time for each other when we were younger with the kids, we worked harder than ever these days, and our work life balance wasn't the best.

'If you want to.' I smiled.

Sebastian smiled, tapped me on the bum, and walked off upstairs to the bedroom.

I got myself a glass of water and followed.

I undressed and got into bed whilst waiting for Sebastian to come out of the bathroom. As normal, he soon after appeared undressing himself as he walked across the bedroom. We snuggled up to each other and started kissing. Sebastian ran his hands through my hair whilst tossing his body on top of mine.

'I love you so much,' Sebastian whispered as he slowly entered inside me whilst still kissing me on the lips. It hurt as he pushed his penis inside me; my vagina was dry these days. It was very rare we had foreplay, mostly straight sex. I didn't tell Sebastian it hurt. I didn't want him to think there was anything wrong or for him to think I wasn't turned on by him.

I wrapped my legs around his body. We both started to moan together as Sebastian pushed his penis faster and harder into me.

'I'm coming, I'm coming,' he shouted.

The room then went quiet for a while, and we lay still in silence. I hadn't come. I didn't say anything, and he didn't ask; it was all over in ten minutes.

Sebastian kissed me on the neck, then on the forehead. 'That was lovely.'

He slowly lifted himself off me and went off to the bathroom for a shower.

'Shall I leave the shower running for you,' he shouted from the bathroom.

'Yes, that would be great,' I shouted back.

I slowly lifted myself out of bed and headed for the bathroom. Sebastian was just stepping out of the shower, ready for me to step in.

The remainder of the Sunday was chilling. I cooked a pork Sunday roast, and we snuggled on the sofa watching films on Netflix.

CHAPTER 2

MONDAY
16ᵀᴴ MARCH 2020

Monday morning came round so fast. I got up at 5.00 am and did a DVD body pump session for forty minutes. I tried to do three sessions a week to keep in shape. I was the big fifty this year, and I found it much harder to keep in shape than when I was younger. Most days I felt fat particularly around my tummy. At least I was trying to do something, I kept telling myself 'If I could just maintain my current weight,' I would say to myself.

The alarm went off at 6.15 am, the same as everyday Monday to Friday. Sebastian and I seemed to be in the same routine during the week. The alarm went off, we got into some slacks, walked for about a half hour to get some exercise; it was then a shower around 7.00 am and both off to work. I worked in an office not too far away whilst Sebastian still worked as a nutritionist and personal trainer. Sebastian loved to keep himself very fit, which is why I felt I must try with my weight training. I had a guilt trip if I didn't exercise. I had it in my head that if I didn't, he wouldn't fancy me anymore, a bit of a stupid thing to think really; it was probably menopausal.

I did question whether I was in the menopause or it was something else. I found myself easily frustrated and anxious over the simplest of things. I didn't have any patience these days and got very emotional and often burst into tears for no apparent reason. Then there were the hot sweats at night… these had been going on for about twelve months. I got rather embarrassed about it all and would never dare talk about it to Sebastian.

'I can deal with this my own way,' I would tell myself.

My monthly periods were also changing. I was either three days late or three days early, I had intermittent bleeding between periods. Deep down I knew I should get it checked out at the doctors, but I chose to dismiss it; the thought of an internal examination and all that messing put me off. I wasn't the best at smear tests, never mind anything else.

I'd just finished my DVD body pump training when Sebastian appeared in the doorway.

'Ready, babe, for a walk?' he asked

'Yes, be with you in five.'

I drank a glass of water, then put on my hoody, ready for a walk.

We walked together holding hands around the lanes for about a half hour. We didn't talk about much when we walked; it was nice to have the silence and not have to think at all.

After our walk, I showered and got ready for work. Most mornings, it took a while to get ready. I looked fat in everything and tried on so many outfits. I got frustrated with myself pulling one top off to try another. I would end up hotter than before I showered and my hair would look such a mess, as if I hadn't done it. I don't know why I didn't sort my outfit out the night before to save all the hassle.

'Why am I so disorganised?' I would ask myself.

This was a regular routine most mornings, trying different outfits, having to do my hair twice, and running late for work.

Sebastian shouted, 'I'm off to work, hun; have a good day. See you later.'

I shouted back, 'Yea, okay.'

I got angrier and angrier with myself as I looked in the mirror. I felt like a bag of shit and looked like one. My tummy looked huge in the skirt I had on, and my boobs seemed to be drooping more than ever in the top. I often wondered whether some of my weight problem was from having a C-Section during giving birth. I can still feel the scar, and it looked flabby around that area. I was probably just making excuses.

I didn't have any more time to mess about.

'I look as good as it gets,' I would tell myself.

I didn't have breakfast, hoping I would lose some pounds if I gave it a miss. I grabbed my bag and keys and left the house for work. The drive wasn't too far, whilst driving I started thinking to myself whether we would get to Goa in the April, I was ready for a holiday. I had cancelled my holiday time booked at work hoping to move it April.

Whilst daydreaming, I forgot about all my troubles of menopause; the traffic I was in, and I arrived at work on the car park without knowing it. I hadn't even noticed whether the traffic lights had been green or red. I had been in my own little world.

I locked the car up and strolled into the office to my desk. The first thing I did every morning when I got to the office was to make myself a nice brew; today was no different. I made a brew and logged on to my computer.

I was usually one of the first in the office, which gave me chance to catch up on my emails. I worked in an open plan office managing a small finance team for a sales call centre. In total there was about fifty staff in the office, so it could get very noisy at times.

I started to focus and plan my diary for the week.

'Good morning, Charlie,' I heard.

I looked up to see Jenny, a member of my team had arrived.

'Oh, good morning, Jenny; did you have a good weekend?'

'Oh yes, lovely, thank you. Went to see my mom with the kids. We had a lovely meal,' she replied.

'That sounds nice.'

'Yes, weather wasn't too bad. She lives in a lovely village called Acton Trussell. It is nice to go walking around there, and there is a beautiful lake. How about you?' she asked.

'We had friends over and drank and ate far too much as usual.' I laughed.

Jenny smiled and laughed.

Emily and Jane arrived together in the office; these were the other two members of my team. I had three in total.

'Morning, Emily; morning, Jane,' I shouted.

'Morning, Charlie,' they shouted back.

'Bet you're hoping they open the Indian borders up soon,' Emily said.

'Definitely am,' I replied. 'I know the borders are closed now due to the pandemic, but I'm hoping they will re-open in April and we'll go out then.'

Jenny popped up. 'I'm not sure you know; the virus has been all over the news, and I think it's really bad here in the UK. I wonder whether we will go into lockdown?'

'My friend was talking about that the weekend,' I replied. 'I just can't see it happening and everything shutting down.'

I looked at my watch and saw it was 9.30 am.

'Sorry, ladies, got to go late for a meeting,' I shouted as I dashed off across the office with my note pad.

Every Monday morning, we had a senior leadership team meeting to discuss the results for the previous week and priorities for the current week. I would start off giving an update on revenue for the previous week and month to date versus budget. It was then over to the sales and marketing teams to give an update on performance, promotions, and events. This took up most of the meeting most weeks.

This week was a little different. The CEO wanted to discuss the coronavirus pandemic and a contingency plan in the likelihood of a lockdown. The business sold windows and doors directly to customers and installers; it was a family run business that had always performed extremely well.

Joe, the CEO, opened the meeting. 'I'd like to cover the immediate impact on the business should the UK go into lockdown. We have heard on the news today that the number of cases in hospitals is significantly growing from the pandemic, and we may well follow other countries.'

He went on to say, 'I'd like us to explore today what options we have and model our options including our worst-case scenario. James, you, and I will work together with the teams this morning on options and inputs. Charlie, I would like you to pull together a worst- and best-case scenario forecast including a cash flow this afternoon once you have all the inputs from us. Is everyone clear with that?'

We all nodded. You could see the anxiety building up in the room. What would our options be? We sell and fit windows and doors.

Joe went on to say, 'Right, James, you, Steve, Dave, and Jimmy will stay in here while we map out our contingency plan. Everyone else can leave. Charlie, we will have something for you to model after lunch. Let us all reconvene in the Boardroom at 4.00 pm. Does that give you enough time, Charlie, to do all the financial modelling?'

I replied, 'Err, yes. I'll set the excel models up this morning so that I can drop the numbers in this afternoon.'

Joe sighed. 'Great.'

Joe looked under a huge amount of pressure, not his usual bubbly self. I left the boardroom and went back to my desk.

'Everything okay,' Emily shouted to me. 'Quick meeting today.'

I could feel my heart palpitating faster and started to feel very anxious.

'I've got to do some financial modelling in case we go into lockdown.'

Jane jumped in, 'It's all over the news; have a look on the internet. My husband works for an IT company, and they are all prepared ready to work from home. They did a test last Friday where everybody worked from home to make sure all the systems worked, and everyone could get access.'

'I don't know how we could work from home, do you, Charlie'? Emily asked.

'I'm not sure really; that's what the team are working on now. I suppose the sales team could still sell,' I replied.

'Do you want a brew, Charlie, before you start getting into all those financial models'? Emily asked.

'I'd love one, thanks—it will keep me going.'

I noticed one of the main doors to the office propped open. It is normally locked to prevent strangers entering and staff have passcodes.

'Who left that door open?' I asked.

Jane replied, 'Oh, it's our health and safety officer. He said that we should not touch door handles, if possible; you can pick up the virus from door handles apparently. They have also put hand wash around the office.'

This was scary stuff, security doors wedged open, contingency plans, hand wash everywhere.

I could see that staff was also talking in little huddles about the coronavirus and about what might happen.

I got the internet up on my computer to see what the updates were. Everything was about the coronavirus and the number of cases; the news talked about what the UK could be facing. It mentioned that there would be an update late that afternoon from Downing Street.

I felt physically sick. I was sure many others did in the office.

I started to get on with Excel models and prepare for the afternoon meetings.

Every time I looked up from my desk, I could see group huddles talking about a potential lockdown and what would happen.

We were all so anxious. I didn't have any lunch, not because of my weight, I hadn't thought about it since the morning but because my stomach was turning with worry and the unknown of a lockdown or what would happen at work.

At lunchtime, I stepped outside to call Sebastian.

'Have you heard about a lockdown being imminent and there's announcements later?'

'Yes, I have; the talk is that gyms and social things like pubs and restaurants will have to close.'

'Oh, my goodness,' I replied, 'where would that leave you?'

Sebastian shouted, 'I don't know; we don't know anything at the moment, Charlie.'

'I'm only asking; no need to shout. I am having to do some scenario planning here today in case of a shutdown. I really don't know what's going to happen.'

'Look, I've got to go; let us talk when we're home. Keep your chin up. Love you lots,' he said.

'Love you too, see you later.' I don't think he listened to what I said; nothing unusual these days.

I returned to my desk to carry on with task in hand.

It was around 2.00 pm when my email pinged. It was an email from Joe, outlining the worse and best-case scenarios for me to crunch the numbers.

I scanned over the plans, not particularly good reading. Worse case was to lay off all of the staff and temporary close the business, and the best-case scenario was to lay off all of the installation team and keep skeleton sales staff to sell future windows and doors for a post lockdown.

I knew this was highly confidential and not to be shared with anyone. This was people's jobs at risk. How would they react in the office if they had site of these plans?

I sat quietly at my desk and started to crunch through some of the numbers. The scenario's assumed no revenue for eight weeks and then a gradual increase for the following months until back up to full capacity.

At 4.00 pm, I went back to the boardroom to present my finding to Joe. He sat very solemnly, as though he knew what I was about to present.

Both scenarios showed that there was a cash deficit. We would need somehow to borrow money from the bank or another source for the business to survive. With no revenue and the fixed costs of rent and rates continuing, we only had enough cash reserves to see us through a couple of months.

James was messing on his phone while we were discussing the plans. He then suddenly interrupted me.

'That's it, Boris Johnson advises everyone in the UK against "non-essential" travel and contact with others and suggests people should avoid pubs, clubs, theatres, and work from home if possible. At this stage, these are merely suggestions. He warns that other vulnerable groups, including pregnant women and those with underlying conditions, may be asked to self-isolate.'

The room was silent for a short while.

Joe sat back in his chair, and after a short pause, he said, 'Inform all staff not to come into the office tomorrow and to make sure they take all their laptops home with them tonight and anything they need to work from home. We will communicate on next steps to all colleague's tomorrow. James we will keep the installation team going for now.'

Everyone gathered their things off the boardroom table and scurried to inform staff of the decision before they left for the evening.

I called my team together to my desk.

'Boris is advising no non-essential travel and for businesses to work from home. Joe has said that from tomorrow all office staff will work from home, so can you make sure you take your laptops home and anything else you need.'

Emily replied, 'Bloody hell, this is serious, I feel sick.'

I could see other teams in the office gathering their things together to leave the office; the office had suddenly got rather louder with everyone rushing around in a panic. It felt like the world was about to end.

I heard someone shout, 'See you all the other side,' as they left the office.

I gathered my laptop and a few files together in my briefcase. I was one of the last to leave the office. I took one final look around and thought when will I see this office again, if at all. I drove home in a daze, trying to come to terms with all what has happening.

When I arrived home, Sebastian had the TV on, listening to Boris on the news. This was it; I was now at home not knowing what was going to happen next.

Sebastian and I talked all night about the pandemic, our jobs, had we enough savings to cover us and were our children safe.

I have to say this is one of the most difficult times we have faced not only as individuals but as a nation.

That night, I hardly slept. I kept looking at my iPad to see if there were any further developments on the coronavirus.

Monday 16th March will always be a day I will never forget.

CHAPTER 3

TUESDAY 17TH MARCH 2020

I still got up at my usual time for work. I decided not to get dressed and kept my PJ's on, this saved around a half hour not having to decide what to wear and changing in and out of outfits.

Sebastian went off to work as normal for now; most gyms remained open, so for him it was life as usual for the time being.

Shortly after 9.00 am Joe called me.

He spoke very calmly. 'Charlie, we need to plan for the worse here. I need to you to think about everything you can do from a finance perspective to retain cash. You need to do another few cash flow forecasts thinking about holding back payments for rent and rates and taking out all non-essential expenditure. I need to start thinking about bank loans and overdrafts sooner than later.'

It was all overwhelming and frightening. We had about fifty employee livelihoods at stake. What about their families? What if they got the pandemic? How about us? Will we survive?

My mind was chasing away with me; at times, I could hardly breathe. Every time I watched the news, I got more scared and anxious.

That day, IT helped us set up Microsoft teams and Zoom to enable us to continue with regular meetings. The rest of the day, I worked through cash flow after cash flow looking at where we could save money. The sales team for now continued to work from home. I had no idea how long we could continue for them to do this.

It felt like a long day for a Tuesday, my head was banging, and I struggled to concentrate. My eyes also felt sore and dry. I guess it is working through so many spreadsheets. I had not slept well the night before either, so I was overtired and irritable. I didn't eat all day; my stomach was in knots.

Sebastian arrived home around 5.00 pm. 'Hiya, hun, how's your day been?'

'Okay,' I shouted back from the home office.

He popped his head around the office door. 'You still working?'

'What does it look like? Just because I'm working from home doesn't mean I'm not busy!'

'God, I only asked.' He shrugged as he walked off into the kitchen. 'What's for dinner?' he shouted

Why did I always get asked that question? I worked too, surely; he could do dinner for a change. I chose to ignore him.

He popped his head back round the office. 'Did you hear me, babe? What's for dinner?'

That was like a red rag to a bull. I had very little patience with Sebastian these days.

'Why do I always do the f'cking dinner. For once, can you not use your brain and decide for yourself?' I yelled.

'Charlie, I only asked. What's wrong with you? I won't ask you anything else.'

'I'm tired, up to my neck in workload, and the last thing on my mind is food right now,' I snarled.

'You sound stressed. Do you fancy a walk to clear your head and exercise?'

'No, I don't; my head is fine, and anyway, why do I need to exercise? I don't have time like you are prancing around at the gym all day. And anyway, are you saying I need to exercise to get some weight off?'

Sebastian walked off mumbling. All I heard was 'Can't even talk to you these days.'

I sighed and ignored the comment. I worked a little later, then logged off for the night.

I didn't fancy a big meal, so I did myself some cheese on toast with brown sauce! This was my favourite. I always craved bread if I felt a bit down.

I cracked open a bottle of white wine and poured a large glass.

Sebastian sorted himself a salmon salad. He was always conscious about eating healthy, no different from when he was younger. We both sat in the lounge, separately on different sofas with our food on trays on our laps.

'Is the wine nice?' Sebastian asked.

'Yep, very nice,' I answered as I took a big swig.

The news was on TV talking about the pandemic.

'Can we have something else on?' I asked. 'I could do with a break from hearing about Covid-19.'

'Anything you want on?'

'Nope, anything but this.'

The air was still a bit frosty between us.

I guzzled the rest of my glass of wine, finished my cheese and toast, then moved into the kitchen and washed the plates.

'Shall I have another glass of wine,' I thought.

'Why not,' I told myself.

Sebastian commented, 'You're knocking that wine back tonight.'

'And? Do you have a problem with that?'

'No, just saying, that's all.'

I didn't understand what the issue was here. What's wrong with a glass of wine? I thought. Anything to pick fault with me.

I necked my glass of wine back in no time whilst watching some crap on the TV Sebastian had put on.

'Well, I might as well top my glass up with what wine is left in the bottle, be rude not to,' I said laughing as I walked back into the kitchen.

I didn't get a reply. Sebastian ignored me. I polished off the last bit of wine in the kitchen.

'Right, I'm off to bed now,' I shouted to Sebastian.

'Okay, I'll lock up and switch everything off. Be up shortly,' he shouted back.

I must have dozed off before Sebastian came to bed, probably lack of sleep from the night before or too much wine!

I woke up at 3.00 am so hot and sweating. I kicked the quilt off and went into the bathroom to wash my face. My hair had gone all curly as I had sweated so much. I looked in the mirror.

'I look like something from Annie,' I thought.

I opened some windows and lay on top of the bed. I tried to get back off to sleep but couldn't. I reached for my iPad off the bedside cabinet and searched for coronavirus update. The news was depressing in Italy and Spain, not much better in the UK either.

I looked at the time, it was now 4.30 am on Wednesday 18th March. Sebastian was lying on his back, snoring; it was starting to annoy me. I nudged him with my elbow.

'You're snoring.'

He made a grunt and turned on his side, which seemed to do the trick.

I lay awake for a long time, or at least it felt like a long time. My tummy started churning and I had sharp pains. In the end, about 5.30 am, I got up.

I went into the bathroom to the toilet. Whilst on the toilet, I started my period; this was four days earlier than my due date, this was all I needed now with everything else going on. Why did I have to be early, at least there may have been chance of some sex if I could have waited until the Saturday.

I sorted myself out then went downstairs to get some painkillers to ease my stomach cramps. I made myself a nice brew as normal and sat waiting until Sebastian got up.

'Alright for a walk, Charlie?'

'Hmm, yes.'

We went off walking as normal before our normal work routine started all over again.

Well, that is if you can call things normal at the moment.

Chapter 4
Wednesday 18th March 2020

'See you later, babe, love you,' Sebastian shouted as he left the house with his sports bag.

'Yes, see you later; have a good day, love you,' I shouted back.

I had a shower and got back into some clean PJ's, no need to get dressed or do my make-up or hair, I wasn't leaving the house at all, I was only moving into the office to work again. This appeared to be my normal routine.

I was pleased I hadn't got to get ready; my tummy was very swollen, and I felt drained. This was regular symptoms I had been feeling for a while when my periods started.

I logged on and thought, here goes another crazy day. It was not long before Joe was on the phone.

'Charlie, I've got a few more scenarios to run through your models. I also want you to do a forecast to year end December. You have January and February actuals, so it should be easy to forecast for the full year.'

'Yes, Joe, I can do that. It might take me the rest of the day to work through.'

'If you can make that your priority today, Charlie, that would be great.'

I had done that many scenarios. I didn't know whether I was coming or going, but still I'd get on with what I was being asked.

Shortly after my mobile rang, it was Summer, our daughter.

'Hi, Mom, how are you?'

'I'm okay, working from home now with all this coronavirus. How is it in the hospital?'

'Yea just spoke to Dad, he said you were at home. I am surprised Dad's still out working at the gyms; it's not exactly essential travel, is it? It's getting busy with coronavirus cases in the hospital, some wards are now sectioned off just for covid-19 patients.'

'Blimey me, I didn't realise it was getting that bad in the hospitals. Yea, you know your dad, he loves the gyms and his work. He loves the gym more than me.' I laughed.

'of course, he doesn't, Mom' Summer laughed. 'It's your imagination; he loves you dearly. I'm off today back on twelve hour shifts tomorrow.'

'I bet you're looking forward to the break today.'

'Yep, done three twelve-hour shifts back to back; I'm shattered. The ICU is getting busy with Covid patients too. Have you heard from Mitch?' Summer asked.

'No, not heard from him since last week. I know he is busy with work supporting businesses, and he was away with friends the weekend. He sent me a message not long ago to say he'll call in the weekend. He's also working from home now like me.'

'Oh, good. It's Mother's Day the weekend, so no doubt I'll see him at yours. A lot of people are now working from home,' she said.

'I forgot about Mother's Day with all the other stuff going on in the world. It'll be lovely to see you both.'

'Okay, Mom, I've got to go. I have got food shopping to do and other jobs.'

'Okay, flower, if I don't hear from you before I'll see you the weekend. Lots of love.'

'Love you too, Mom, bye bye.'

Summer works for the NHS. I worried so much about her at work. She is so young at twenty to be having to see all this with the pandemic; she is a strong person, though.

Mitch, our son, works for a bank on the business side. He too is working from home and very busy supporting businesses. He is now twenty-five years old, slightly older than Summer. He enjoys the gym like his dad and keeps himself looking good. I think he is a very handsome young man; all mothers would say that about their sons.

Well, I had better get on with my work, I thought.

I spent the rest of the day churning through numbers on spreadsheets. My head was still spinning, and I could feel the anxiety increasing.

The day went so quickly. I looked up at the time and it was 3.45 pm. I had a Microsoft teams call with my Finance team planned for 4.00 pm. I got myself a hot drink ready to start my meeting.

It felt strange having a meeting on the laptop. I clicked on the teams invite, and hey, bingo, I could see all my finance team.

'Hi, everyone, how are you all doing?' I asked.

Emily was the first to speak. 'Yea, I'm good, thanks; feels a bit strange not being in the office.'

Jane asked, 'I wonder how long we will be like this for, Charlie?'

'I'm not sure,' I replied. 'Joe hasn't said much more apart from asking me to do some more financial modelling.'

Jenny asked, 'It's all a bit overwhelming all of this. They keep saying on the news that we haven't hit the peak yet. Have you seen all that with Spain and Italy? It's awful. I hope we don't get it that bad. It's worrying times for all of us.'

Jenny was a bit of a worrier and enjoyed being part of a team; she would miss all the office banter.

I suggested, 'I think we should put a couple of teams meetings in the diary a week, maybe a Monday and a Thursday. We can talk about priorities for the week and anything else in general, even if there's nothing to update on we can have a quick chat. And anything you want in the meantime please pick the phone up to me.'

I knew this would be some reassurance for Jenny that she was not on her own. She lived alone, so the office was her social life.

'I'll organise those invites, Charlie,' Jenny said.

'Great, thank you, Jenny,' I replied.

We talked about general chit chat for the remaining twenty minutes, making each laugh best we could. It had only been two days working from home, and it already felt like a lifetime. How long would this go on for? I thought.

At 5.15 pm, Sebastian arrived home from work.

He popped his head around the office door and gave me a kiss on the cheek asking, 'Good day, my dear'?

'Yes, all good, thanks,' I replied.

Before I had chance to say how about you, he continued, 'You look tired. Are you in a better mood than last night?'

Why did he have to spoil the conversation? Last night was fine. I didn't see what the problem was and why he asked that question.

'What do you mean by that?' I asked

'Oh, nothing,' he replied as he walked off.

I followed him into the kitchen. 'No, come on, what do you mean by that?'

'Nothing, for goodness sake, Charlie. I just asked if you were better than last night.'

I angrily replied, 'I was fine last night, and I'm fine today.'

Sebastian ignored me. I hated it when he did that; he brushed past me and went off upstairs for a shower.

What is it with men, they have no understanding of how you feel when you're on your period. Why can't they be positive and say something nice for a change. Something like you smell nice or I have missed you today.

I felt tearful tonight; I don't know why. Maybe it was all this going on with the pandemic and the unknown or was it my monthly cycle or was it both. Goodness knows.

I logged off and went upstairs. I hadn't finished the forecast for Joe I promised, but I couldn't be arsed to carry on.

I started to run a hot bath whilst Sebastian was in the shower.

I went back downstairs again, contemplating opening a bottle of wine. Why not, I told myself. I wasn't going anywhere soon, and a glass would be nice in the bath.

Sebastian stepped out of the shower as I entered to turn the bath off. I looked at him, and I must admit, he still did have a good fit body. Sebastian looked at himself in the mirror in the bedroom whilst drying himself.

'I could do with getting a few pounds off.'

'You're having a laugh,' I replied. 'You want to look at me if you think your fat.'

'You're not fat,' he replied, laughing. 'I love you as you are.'

He grabbed me and put his arms around me kissing me on the head.

'Do you fancy some fun?' he whispered in my ear.

'Not really.'

'Do you want to play with me?' he whispered.

'In your dreams.' I laughed

I picked my wine glass up and walked off to bathroom.

'You on the wine again?'

'You know I am; you've just seen me with the glass.'

'You're a bit of a wino this week, Mrs Dyson.'

I didn't bite back; I kicked the bathroom door shut with my foot. I had decided to put some candles on and some music while I had a hot, soapy bath.

It felt lovely and relaxed for a change. A song played on the radio 'Dancing with my Father' by Luther Vandross; this reminded me of my dad. I started to cry, and tears ran down my face. The memories flooded back of when I was a child and my dad shouting at me for bringing tar in the house on my shoes, great memories.

I had no idea what was wrong with myself lately. I got really emotional and started to cry at the simplest of things. If I knew I was going to cry, I would go somewhere where I was on my own. I hated crying in front of people; I felt stupid.

'Are you ok up there?' Sebastian shouted.

I wiped my eyes on the towel and replied, 'Yes, I'm getting out now, won't be long.'

I didn't want Sebastian to see me like this.

I quickly got out of the bath, dried myself, and sorted myself out with a tampon.

Sebastian has no idea I was on my period and probably wouldn't until the weekend. I often wondered whether other middle-aged couples talked about things like this or how often they had sex. Were we good or bad? I thought. I'll hold onto that thought.

I went downstairs to find Sebastian had prepared some dinner, nothing special, but at least he'd tried. He'd prepared a lovely ploughman's salad with some garlic bread. I must admit it looked very tasty, and he had made an effort. We both sat in the lounge again on separate sofas to eat our meals. I also poured another glass of wine. Sebastian looked but said nothing.

'Summer called today,' I said.

'Yes, I spoke to her too.'

'She said the hospital is getting really busy with covid patients.'

'I don't know where all this will end up over the coming weeks. The gyms still seem busy now as if nothing's happening, but I can't see this continuing for much longer.'

I asked, 'Does the disease spread more easily in gyms with all that sweating?'

'I guess so, but I'm no expert ,Charlie.'

After dinner, we put a film on. It wasn't really my kind of film; it was a film about a drug cartel, not something I'm interested in but definitely Sebastian's kind of film. I finished off the wine in the bottle, then same as last night, I went off up to bed first.

'Just finishing the end of this film, babe, then I'll be up,' Sebastian said.

'Okay, no worries,' I replied as I walked up the stairs.

I felt so tired after not sleeping well for a few nights. I was also conscious that I had to get up early to finish off this forecast for work that I should have done today.

CHAPTER 5

THURSDAY
19TH MARCH 2020

I woke up early again today at 5.45 am. I slept all through the night, which was good for me. I turned to Sebastian; he was still fast asleep. I had no idea what time he came to bed. Sebastian always slept in the nude and always ended up with the quilt off him by the morning. I found it amusing to see him lying there naked with all his bits hanging.

I laughed to myself and thought, should I just grab his penis for a joke and make him jump. I decided not to. He probably wouldn't find it as amusing as me; funny how the stupidest things tickled me these days!

Bang on 6.00 am, the alarm went off. Sebastian puts his arm to the side without opening his eyes and switched it off.

'Good morning, happy Thursday,' I said.

'Hmmm, happy Thursday be even better if it was Friday.'

'Don't wish your life away,' I replied, laughing.

I was the first out of bed and downstairs to make a hot brew. It took Sebastian about a half hour to get out of bed, go to the toilet, have a wash, brush his teeth, and eventually get dressed.

'Up for a walk?' Sebastian asked whilst making a cup of coffee.

'Yep, I'll just go pop on my tracksuit.'

I was ready in five minutes with my hair scraped back in a bun. There is a big lake close to where we live. We had decided to walk to the lake and around it before returning; this took us about half an hour.

As soon as we were back, I jumped into the shower and put clean PJ's on, same routine as the previous days, at least I wasn't hating myself for not fitting in my clothes; that was one consolation. I could slob around in my PJ's to my heart's content with the house to myself.

I had a call at 10.00 am with Joe, so I got my head down to finish this forecast. I hadn't long started my work when Sebastian popped his head around the office door.

'I'm off now, babe; have a good day. See you later.'

I turned around; he blew me a kiss. he looked very smart in a new tracksuit I got him for Christmas.

'Looking very smart, Mr D,' I said.

'Not wore this yet so I thought I'd give it a bash. Great present from my lovely wife.'

I smiled at him. 'Have a good day; love you lots.'

I didn't have the stomach cramps today, which was a bonus; hopefully, my day would be as good as it can be. I finished off the forecast; it didn't matter how I cut the plans, cash was very tight. I couldn't magic a miracle, and I didn't have a crystal ball to predict the future.

Will installation carry on? Stop for two months? Will the sales team still sell? None of us knew this.

I emailed the forecast to Joe ready for our call.

Whilst waiting to go on our teams meeting, I decided to look at the news on the internet. I hadn't looked at much the last few days. Gosh nearly three thousand people had now died in Italy from coronavirus. Iran, Belgium, and France also had their highest recorded cases. The death toll in the UK from the virus was now at 104. It was all depressing news around the globe.

On the call at 10.00 am, Joe asked me to talk through the forecast and assumptions. James, our operation director, was also on the meeting but didn't say much. I decided not to show my face on the teams meeting. I didn't want them to see me with no make-up, hair tied back and wearing my PJ's. I talked through the profit and loss and cash flow referring to an assumption tab I'd put in. I'd built the forecast so that we could change any assumptions and it fed into the profit and loss and cash flow automatically.

I stated, 'The difficulty here, Joe, are the unknowns. I can keep changing the numbers, but we don't know what is going to happen over the next couple of weeks.'

'I know that, Charlie; you don't have to state the bloody obvious,' Joe snapped. 'You've assumed people in here are being laid off; have you put redundancy costs in?'

'I haven't, no.'

'Why not? Surely, you have to put that in the cash flow. Have you assumed a deferred payment the VAT and PAYE?'

'Err, no, I haven't. I can do that if you wish?' I asked.

'Charlie, get your act together. I can't do your job for you. I need you to think out of the box of everything we can do to keep this business going,' Joe shouted.

I didn't say anything back. I could feel tears building up in my eyes.

'Are you okay with that?' Joe asked.

'Yes,' I replied, fighting back the tears.

'Good, send something over by end of the day. James stay on the meeting; we need to discuss operational plans.' he yelped.

I ended the call and burst into tears. I cried so much my eyes were all red and sore. I should have just done it I told myself. Joe is under enough stress without having to tell me what to do. I needed to pull myself together. I beat myself up over lots of things like this these days.

It was Thursday, so I had another team meeting at 11.00 am with my finance team. I put some make-up around my eyes to cover up the redness and quickly stuck a zip up jacket on over my PJ's.

I clicked the button to join the meeting to see they were all waiting for me.

'Hey, Charlie, how are you?' Jenny asked.

'Yes, I am good, thanks. It was only yesterday we all spoke, but are you all okay?' I asked.

'Yes, yes, we're okay,' they all said at the same time.

'Good, can everyone access their files okay? No problems with IT at all?' I asked.

They all replied simultaneously 'Yes, we can access everything.'

We spent the next fifteen minutes chewing over the fat about the coronavirus and the news in other countries.

I was glad to end the call. I still felt very tearful and was having a hot flush. I flung my jacket off as soon as I got off the call.

I went to the bathroom and washed my face in cold water. I looked in the mirror as I dried my face. I looked like a red tomato! My cheeks were bright red, and my eyes swollen and red.

I got myself a glass of water and sat back at my desk. My mobile pinged; it was Sebastian texting me.

'Hi. babe, hope you're having a good day. If you get chance could you put my tracksuit in the laundry basket in the wash. Thanks so much. my lovely. You are a star. Love you. Xx.'

I texted back, 'No worries. I'll sort it. Okay, love you lots, xx.'

I didn't want to tell him about the tearful morning; he'd probably just say pull yourself together. Sebastian only saw the hard side of me and not the emotional states I got into lately.

After putting the washing in, I sat back down in the office to get on with this forecast. I spent the rest of the day on the forecast model delaying as many payments as possible. I put a call into HR to discuss average redundancy payments to plug that into the model. How realistic delaying all these creditors was I didn't know, and the number of redundancies was still an unknown. It still didn't give us a positive cash forecast. I wasn't a miracle worker!

I decided to send the revised model across to Joe at 4.55 pm so that I wouldn't have to go through it again today on a call. I couldn't face Joe shouting at me again.

I needed to cheer myself up. I hadn't eaten all day, so decision made, it was my turn to get in the kitchen. I looked in the cupboards and found a Bolognese sauce and some pasta.

Sebastian arrived home about 6.00 pm. 'Heya, babe, how are you? Something smells nice,' he shouted as he walked in the door.

'Yes, I've cooked your favourite spaghetti Bolognese, my dear.'

Sebastian got the spoon; he tasted the sauce. 'Hmmmm, that's tasty.'

'I like you in that tracksuit.'

'Yes, I quite like me as well.' He laughed

'Good day?' I asked.

'Yes, I've got some new clients. I'm working from home tomorrow; I have a few dietary plans to do for some people.'

'Oh, that's good. Go shower then we can have a proper catch up with our dinner.'

Sebastian winked. 'Okay, won't be long.'

There was no way I was going to tell him about my day. I was so glad he hadn't been working from home today. I prayed tomorrow would be a better day.

I dished up while Sebastian was in the shower. I even put a little bit of parsley on the top for decoration. We both sat as usual on separate sofa's, munching away on our food. Sebastian had the remote control and kept flicking through programs to see what was on TV.

'I'm so glad it's Friday tomorrow,' I sighed.

'Me too,' Sebastian replied.

'It's been a long week; feels like I've been working from home for weeks and it's only been a few days.'

Sebastian didn't reply and carried on flicking through channels.

'Are you listening to me or am I talking to myself?' I asked.

'Sorry, babe, just seeing what's on. What did you say?'

'Forget it; I'm not repeating myself.'

Sebastian looked over. 'Don't be like that. What was it you were saying?'

'Nothing,' I yelled.

I grabbed my food and headed off to the kitchen to eat it. Sebastian came in ten minutes later with an empty dish.

'I don't know what's wrong with you lately, Charlie. You are so up and down; I'm frightened to say anything.'

'Yea, always my fault, never yours.'

Sebastian sighed. 'Here we go again. Come sit with me, and we'll have a chat.'

'It doesn't matter,' I replied. 'Forgot what I was saying now.'

Sebastian shook his head and walked back into the lounge.

I decided to sit in the kitchen and open a bottle of prosecco. I preferred prosecco to wine these days. My taste buds had changed the last few months. I used to love carling but found that sickly and now preferred cider.

I got through a few glasses in no time whilst playing on my mobile catching up on Facebook and sending a few messages.

At 10.00 pm, Sebastian popped into the kitchen. 'I'm off to bed. Are you coming up?'

'In a bit,' I replied without even looking up from my phone.

He didn't reply and went off up to bed. I finished off the prosecco and started to cry again. I wanted Sebastian to come and put his arms around me. Maybe he didn't fancy me anymore, and I'm not as attractive as when I was younger. I knew I'd put some weight on, all this started going through my head again. I'd started to act like a manic depressive and half the time I don't know I'm doing it.

On that note, it was time for bed. Sebastian was already snuggled up fast asleep. I quietly got into bed and snuggled down. I manged to get a couple of hours sleep before I woke up ringing wet with a hot flush.

I cooled down with some cold water and decided to get into the spare bed. I felt really embarrassed when I had these hot flushes and would rather be on my own, I also knew I would have difficulty getting back off to sleep.

CHAPTER 6
FRIDAY 20TH MARCH 2020

Friday morning started off the same as any other workday. I was up first and sitting with a brew when Sebastian woke to the alarm at 6.00 am. Instead of getting straight up out of bed today, he shouted down to me, 'Any chance of a cuppa in bed?'

I guessed this was because he was working from home today and not planning on going out.

'Yea, I'll bring one up,' I shouted back.

I made myself another cup of tea and one for Sebastian. I loved my tea in a morning. I could easily drink four to five cups. I carried both cups of tea upstairs, handed Sebastian his drink, and I sat on the other side of the bed with my drink.

'What's your plan today, babe?' he asked.

'Same as any other Friday, work,' I sighed.

'How about you?' I asked.

'I'm going to get these nutritional plans done this morning, then I might do the lawns this afternoon. Do you need the office this morning?'

'Err, yes, I could do with the office; I've got a call with Joe this morning to go through a forecast, and it may go on a bit.'

The last thing I wanted was a repeat of yesterday. Joe having a go at me and me bursting into tears in the kitchen or the lounge. At least in the office, I could shut the door and be on my own.

'Okay, not a problem. I'll work in the conservatory.'

'Thank you. If we're going for a walk, we need to make a move. I need to get on this call.'

Sebastian nodded. 'Okay, I'm coming now.'

I got off the bed and went into the bathroom to put some slacks on for the walk. After the usual walk, I settled in the office for work, and Sebastian settled in the conservatory. I didn't bother with a shower this morning; it was too late after the walk. I decided to have one later.

I now had daily calls at 9.00 am with Joe, story of my life, what was in store today?

I dialled in on the teams meeting call at 9.00 am. Joe was already on the call.

'We're just waiting for James to join,' he said.

'Okay,' I replied.

'How are you today?'

'Yes, fine. Still feels a bit strange being at home and the not knowing how long this is going to go on for.'

'Hmmm, I think Boris is doing a statement later. Be interesting to hear what he's got to say. There's still lots of people going about their business as usual after his Monday's announcement on recommendations.'

I replied, 'Yes, a bit weird, really. I don't think people know what to do for the best. Sebastian has been working as normal and said the gyms are still busy.'

'Let's see what happens later,' Joe said.

On that note, James joined the meeting.

Joe suggested, 'Okay, let's start off by going through the forecast, Charlie, you've prepared it.'

I spent the next fifteen minutes walking them through my model and assumptions I had applied on potential cash savings.

'Much better, Charlie,' Joe said.

I felt relieved; I had done something right for once.

Joe continued, 'Charlie, you can drop off now. James let's go through your contingency operational plan and agree how we're measuring productivity with the guys working from home.'

I didn't argue to leave the meeting. 'Okay. Have a good weekend if we don't speak again today.'

No one answered, so I ended the meeting. Phew, that was it then now. I could get on with my day job for the rest of the day.

The day went well. Sebastian got on with his nutritional plans and mowed the lawns for the first time. That took him a good few hours; the first cut always takes longer.

Later that day, Boris was on TV to address the nation. I could not believe what he announced.

Boris Johnson ordered all pubs, cafes, restaurants, bars, and gyms to close. The chancellor also announced that the taxpayer will meet eighty percent of the wages of employees temporarily sent home from firms hit by the crisis.

Boris Johnson didn't look well at all; he had tested positive for coronavirus but said he only had mild symptoms and would be self-isolating and working from home.

Sebastian and I just stared at the TV in shock trying to take it all in and work out what that meant for us. One thing that was clear, Sebastian would be out of work. He was self-employed, so how would he get paid eighty percent? What would that mean for me and my work colleagues? I wondered. How would people react to all of hospitality closing?

I could see Sebastian in deep thought.

'I kinda knew something was coming, but I didn't expect them to completely order gyms to close. I thought they may have put some measures in place such as restricted numbers in gyms. I won't be able to work at all,' he said.

I replied 'I know; there's no real details on wages being paid yet. Well, nothing I can see online. They can't ignore the self-employed. They'll have to do something for them too.'

Sebastian started biting his lip. He did this when he wasn't sure about something or had something on his mind. I bet the thought that he couldn't train would be worrying him more than the loss of wages. The gym was his life; he always said it helped him to relax when he trained, it would be the last thing I would think of to help me relax. I exercised but because I felt I needed to not because I wanted to. I could think of better ways to relax, maybe a glass of wine or prosecco would do it for me!

I tried to change the subject. 'What do you fancy doing the weekend?'

'Dunno really. I usually train the weekend, but I can't do that.'

'You've got some weights in the garage.'

'Yes, but not everything I need.'

'Have a look online and see if you can order some,' I suggested.

'Yes, I will. Where's the iPad?'

I had the iPad on my lap. I was looking to see if I could get any more information on the announcement of the eighty percent wages to be paid. I passed Sebastian the iPad

'Here it is.'

Sebastian spent the next half hour browsing the internet. While he was doing that I went and opened a bottle of prosecco. I felt like a drink after listening to Boris, and after all, it was Friday. I asked Sebastian if he wanted a beer, but he said he didn't fancy one.

'Bloody hell, there is gym equipment but the earliest delivery I can get anywhere is May.' Sebastian tutted.

'What? There's nothing earlier than that?'

'Nope, and if you look at places like Argos, they are all out of stock.'

'Maybe leave it then. I would have thought things will have improved by May?'

We left the news on the TV for the rest of the evening. It was all very depressing; the news discussed the announcement, telling us to protect our NHS and only go out for essential travel.

Sebastian decided to have a beer in the end. I think he was feeling down listening to the news. I finished off the bottle of prosecco. My heart was racing. I started to feel numb and sick again. I started to think about Summer working in the hospital. I messaged her.

'Are you okay at work? Been watching the news about Boris's announcement. What is it like in the hospital? Love you lots, xx.'

I didn't get a reply, so I guessed she must be busy. Summer was usually very quick at replying; she was never without her phone.

About ten o'clock, we decided to call it a day and went to bed. I found it difficult to get off to sleep. I lay thinking about what could happen, our jobs, the children at work, what if we got Covid-19? My mind was in overdrive. I felt at times like I couldn't breathe again.

Friday 20th March will be a day to remember in history; this was the start of a UK compulsory lockdown.

CHAPTER 7

SATURDAY
21ST MARCH 2020

I got up early around 5.00 am after another sleepless irritable night. I decided to do a body pump training session to take my mind off things. I usually did a session on a Saturday, Sunday, and a day in the week, depending on workload. After my session, I sat quietly with a hot drink and listened to the 6.00 am news. The news talked solely of Covid-19, only to do essential travel and not to visit our moms on Mother's Day. I must admit, I had forgot about Mother's Day, it seemed irrelevant with everything else going on. I was more concerned that we all got through this safe than having a bunch of flowers.

My health hadn't been brilliant as late. January and February weren't great. I picked up one cold and cough after another. One particular time in February, I was really poorly with a cough and had trouble breathing as if I was suffering with asthma. I'd never had asthma, so goodness knows what it was.

I looked up the symptoms of Covid-19 on my I-pad. It read;

+ shortness of breath
+ a cough that gets more severe over time
+ a low-grade fever that gradually increases in temperature
+ fatigue

Well, I had all the symptoms except for a fever, but then again, in saying that I had hot sweats regularly so wouldn't know the difference. Maybe I had it without knowing, I thought.

Sebastian shouted down to me around 7.00 am.

'Any chance of a cup of tea, babe.'

'Yes, I'll bring one up.'

I heard Sebastian going into the bathroom, same routine as every morning; must be a man thing that they have to go to the toilet as soon as they get up. I put the kettle on and made two cups of tea to take upstairs. By the time I arrived back upstairs with the tea, Sebastian was back in bed.

'Are you coming back to bed, hun?' he asked.

I knew where this was going; it was the weekend. He probably thought we were going to have sex. He'd got another thing coming. I was still on my period. Even more annoying, he didn't even know. Was that normal for a married couple?

I answered, 'Yes, I'll drink my tea in bed. I've just done a fitness session.'

'God, you're early, babe. What time did you get up?'

'Err, about 5.00 am. I didn't sleep too good. I've been listening to the news, it's all about Covid-19. I also forgot it's Mother's Day tomorrow.'

'Oh, yes, I forgot about that too. I wonder if the kids will come over?'

'I doubt it; you're only supposed to go out for essential travel. They are advising people not to travel to see their mothers tomorrow.'

'I wonder how many will take notice of that?' Sebastian said.

'I've looked at the symptoms for Covid-19; it's made me wonder whether I had it back in February when I had that really bad cough and couldn't breathe very well. Do you remember?'

'I do remember it; if you had those symptoms now, I would say yes, but I'm not sure back then because none of us got it. Surely, if it were Covid the kids or I would have got it too?'

'You're probably right, Sebastian; no one else had those symptoms. Maybe I'm just over thinking.'

He pulled me to him. 'Well, stop over thinking and come here.'

Sebastian put his arm around me, kissing me on the neck, then he moved on to kissing me on the lips. His hand slipped under the covers, and he started to rub his hand up and down my leg slowly moving up my nightdress.

'Sorry, not today,' I nodded as I moved his hand away.

'What's wrong?'

'Wrong time of the month, and I shouldn't have to tell you that.'

He sat up quietly, picking up his cup of tea. 'How am I supposed to know?'

'How are you supposed to know? Well, let's start with you are my husband or are you not?'

Sebastian sighed. 'Here we go again. I don't know everything that goes on with you when you're on and off your period. You said you've been a bit all over the place.'

I didn't want to get into a row over this. I got up and took a shower saying nothing else on the matter. By the time I was ready, Sebastian was already downstairs waiting for me.

'Shall we go for a walk, hun,' he asked as he tapped me on the bum.

'Yes, that would be nice.'

We left the house and had a nice leisurely stroll; Saturdays were always peaceful; we were not rushing back for work. Halfway on the walk, Sebastian grabbed hold of my hand. He looked at me and smiled.

'You know I love you.'

'I know.'

'Don't take this personally, Charlie, but do you think you could be in the menopause?'

'What makes you say that?'

'Well, don't take this the wrong the way, Charlie, but you're very moody lately; it's like treading on eggshells. You're like a bottle of pop and go off at anything.'

I didn't reply and kept quiet. We carried on walking; Sebastian still held my hand until we got home. I felt very tearful after what he had said to me. I couldn't wait till we got back to the house. Was I really this bad? I thought. As soon as we were home, I went upstairs into the bathroom and started to cry. I felt like I had pushed my family aside, and that no one had any idea how I felt. I was so exhausted from not sleeping, my energy levels were so low, I had even started picking on cake and chocolate, probably because it gave me some energy. My tastebuds had changed. I was always more of a savoury person enjoying sausage rolls and things like that. I'd very rarely have a dessert if we went for a meal. I hated sugar and sweet things. That's why I was probably putting weight on because I was eating the wrong things.

'Do you want some breakfast?' Sebastian shouted.

I wiped my eyes and consoled myself.

'I'll be down in a minute,' I shouted.

I could smell something nice cooking. When I got downstairs, I found Sebastian cooking bacon and sausage.

'I'm going to have an egg, bacon, and sausage sandwich. Do you want one?' he asked

'You know I don't like sausage.'

'Well, okay then, bacon and egg for you.' He sighed rolling his eyes

'I'll just have one, please.'

'Okay, go and sit down in the lounge. I'll bring it in shortly with a nice cup of tea.'

It's not very often we have a cooked breakfast, so it was a bit of a treat. I forgot about all the calories today; it's probably some comfort eating I needed.

We both sat and ate our sandwich in silence, not much of a conversation at all. When we'd finished, Sebastian took the plates into the kitchen to wash up.

Shortly after my mobile started to ring, it was Summer.

'Hi, Mom, how you doing?'

'I'm good, hun, how are you?'

'Yea, I'm all good. Sorry I didn't text back last night. I worked a long shift and collapsed in bed when I got home.'

'Oh, don't worry. I know you're busy. How's it going in the hospital?'

'It's a bit crazy at the moment. We have a lot of wards just for Covid-19 cases and some routine wards are being closed.'

'Wow, is it really that bad?'

'Yes, and it is expected to get worse and hit a peak in April.'

'That is worrying. We are so worried about you; will you have to work on the Covid-19 wards?'

'Probably, yes, some staff are already being redeployed on those wards. I don't think the staff is happy, but we don't have a choice. It's very depressing, really,' she sighed.

'Surely that's putting NHS staff at risk?'

'It is, but that's the field that we work in. We're just waiting to see what protection we will have because we don't want to be at risk of picking up the virus.'

'I should think not. Surely, all staff should have protective clothing before going on any of these wards?'

'Yep, we'll see. Anyhow, I don't think we can come over tomorrow for Mother's Day given the advice on essential travel.'

'Summer, don't worry about Mother's Day; you have far more important things going on. It's just lovely to talk to you. How is Chris getting on?'

'He's okay, Mom. I've got him decorating the lounge, you know he loves decorating!'

'I bet he loves you; I've never known anyone decorate as much as you two.' I laughed.

'Well, it's got to be done. He's still really busy with work at the moment. I'm not sure the building trade will stop. They work outside so probably a bit different to an office or factory. We'll have to see.'

'You're probably right. I'm finding it strange working from home, and now your dad is going to be at home with all the gyms closing.'

'Of course, god how is he going to get on not being able to train?' Summer laughed

'I know, I think we're going to kill each other.' I laughed.

'Tell Dad I'll call him later and cheer him up.'

'Okay, flower, I will.'

'I'm going to go, Mom; we want to get on with this decorating. I'll give you a bell tomorrow for Mother's Day.'

'Okay, sweetheart, take care and I'll speak to you tomorrow. Love you lots.'

'Love you lots too, Mom. Keep smiling.'

It was so lovely to hear from Summer; it puts all my problems into perspective. When I thought of what must be going on in the hospitals and all those poor people that were poorly with the virus. I did hope we all stayed safe and didn't contract the virus.

Sebastian appeared back into the lounge after washing up.

'Who was you talking to?' he asked.

'It was Summer. She was telling me about how bad it's getting in the hospitals.'

'Really, she's okay, isn't she?'

I nodded. 'She's fine at the minute, but she was saying that some staff are being moved onto Covid-19 wards, and she will probably be moved soon.'

'I hope she tells them that she doesn't want to move, and she's happy on the ward she's on.'

'I don't think she can. She has to go where they put her.'

'I'll talk to her later; I don't want anything happening to my little girl.'

'She said she'll call you later; they're doing some decorating today.'

'What again? I bet Chris is happy,' he joked. 'Have you heard form Mitch?'

'No, I haven't; you know what he's like, though; he probably had a skinful last night!'

Sebastian laughed. 'I don't know who he takes after; it's not me.'

I gave him a dirty look and made no comment.

We kept busy for the rest of the day. I got on with jobs around the house, and Sebastian did some more jobs in the garden. Keeping busy and not listening to the news was probably the best thing; we felt depressed when we listened to the news.

We both sat down to rest around 4.00 pm. We had kept busy all day and felt shattered by the end of it. I sat with my iPad to do our weekly online shop with Tesco. I did the order, which took me twice as long because the site was slow, then only to find out there was no delivery slots, not only for this week but for any week. What was the point in spending the last friggin forty-five minutes doing an order to find out I couldn't get it delivered?

'This is doing my feckin head in,' I shouted.

'What's up?'

'I can't get a delivery slot for our grocery order; there's no slots available for any time.'

'How about click and collect?' Sebastian asked.

'No, not even for that.'

Sebastian laughed. 'Looks like you'll have to starve then.'

'What do you mean by that? I don't eat that much; you're the fat b*****d who eats everything.'

Sebastian looked at me. 'Was there any need to respond like that?'

'Was there any reason to make a comment that I overeat?'

'I never said you overeat; I made a joke that you'll have to starve.'

'You were hinting at my weight.'

'No, I wasn't; your obsessed about how you look. How many times do I have to tell you, I love you as you are? You're getting paranoid and twist everything,' Sebastian said.

'I know how you said it.'

Sebastian nodded and sighed, saying nothing else.

'We'll have to go to the supermarket tomorrow or Monday.'

'Whatever,' Sebastian replied as he walked off upstairs.

Nothing much changed the rest of the day; we watched some TV. I drank a bottle of prosecco, and Sebastian had a few beers.

I had a restless night again, tossing and turning with hot sweats. It was getting to be a regular thing most nights.

CHAPTER 8
SUNDAY 22ND MARCH 2020

Sunday morning was pretty much the same as Saturday morning. I got up, did my fitness session, albeit it was a little later today as I slept until 6.30 am, that was good going considering I hadn't slept particularly well.

For breakfast today I had cereal. I could have eaten another bacon and egg sandwich but needed to watch the calories.

Sebastian got up about 8.00 am and kissed me on the cheek.

'Happy Mother's Day, my darling.' He smiled.

'I'm not your mother.' I laughed.

'No but you've been a great mom to our kids.' He winked

'And to you, I suppose; you're the biggest kid of all.' I laughed

He smiled at me.

'I wonder if the kids will come today?'

'I don't think so with all this social distancing and non-essential travel, it's not the right thing to do. Summer isn't going to risk it, and I'll tell Mitch the same. I wouldn't want them to get into any trouble.'

'I don't think it would hurt them popping over for a half hour, Charlie.'

'I'd rather they didn't, Sebastian. I don't want them to risk it. And you know what the neighbours are like. They both hold responsible jobs and should follow the guidelines.'

'I suppose you're right. We should set an example for them.'

On that, my mobile pinged; it was Mitch texting.

'Happy Mother's Day to the bestest ever Mom, I love you lots and lots and lots. Will call you shortly when I've had some breaky xxxx.'

Mitch was such a charmer, everybody loved him. He works for a bank on the business side, he has been working from home for the past week trying to sort out businesses who are impacted by Covid-19. He lives alone, he doesn't have one particular girlfriend, but I don't think he's short in taking girls out. Mitch loved nights out with his mates. I wondered how he would get on with the pubs shut and not going out socialising. I was very much like Mitch when I was younger, I loved to party at college but worked hard. If Mitch was a girl, he would be a mini me.

'I'll cook a lovely Sunday roast for you today. Go put your feet up; you deserve it,' Sebastian said.

That's probably one of the nicest things he had said in days. I decided to take him up on it, so I moved to the lounge and sat reading some magazines I'd got. Usually for Mother's Day, we would all get together for lunch but not this year; this year was different to any other. It was just Sebastian and me.

I left Sebastian to the kitchen whilst I relaxed and received phone calls from both our lovely children, Summer and Mitch. I felt very lucky to have such lovely children; they have never brought any trouble home, and I was so proud of them. If there was one thing Sebastian and I got right, it was the children.

Summer and Mitch agreed it wasn't worth taking a risk to come see me. We all agreed that when things were more normal, we would all go out and celebrate over a meal and a few drinks. They sent me lovely messages with pictures of pop-up flowers; they were lovely to read.

Around 1.00 pm, I had a delivery to the house. It was a large heavy box that clanged when I carried it. I placed it on the kitchen table and got the scissors to open the box.

Sebastian had got a pinafore on in the kitchen whilst doing the cooking. He looked over.

'Go on then, open it; you love surprises.'

'Do you know what it is?' I asked

'No, haven't got a clue.'

I opened the box carefully to find it was a case of prosecco with some chocolates. There was a note in the box saying 'To the best mom in the world. We love you lots, Happy Mother's Day, love Summer and Mitch, xx.'

It was such a lovely surprise, I never expected anything; they must have planned it between their selves on Friday or yesterday after Boris's announcement. What a lovely thought; it cheered me up a lot.

'Go on then, open a bottle, let's try it,' Sebastian said.

'What now, it's a bit early.' I laughed.

'Never too early on Mother's Day. We've got some orange juice; we'll have a bucks fizz together,' he suggested.

'You want one too?'

'Why not? It's Sunday. I'll open a bottle, you get the glasses.'

I wasn't going to argue with that. I grabbed two prosecco glasses out of the glass cupboard. Sebastian poured us both a drink mixed with orange juice.

'Cheers, Charlie, you are one in a million.'

I smiled and took a sip of my drink.

'Right, dinner will be ready in about an hour, is that okay?'

'Yes, that's good for me. I'll text the kids to thank them, and I'll lay the table for us. Be nice to sit at the table for a change.'

'Super-duper.' Sebastian winked.

I was thrilled with the delivery. I thanked the kids; they were so happy that I got the delivery on time and was enjoying my day.

Sebastian cooked a lovely pork roast with my favourite veg, mash, and roast potatoes and stuffing. Then to finish off, we had cheese and biscuits. We were both so full after eating, we loaded the dishwasher and collapsed on the sofas.

'Let's get a film on,' Sebastian suggested.

'Not a war film.'

'No, you choose today; it's your day.'

I started to flick through Netflix to see if I could find something, but nothing really caught my eye.

Sebastian then suggested, 'There's a series on Netflix called Narcos about a drug cartel. A few people have mentioned it to me and said it's well worth watching. Have a read on it and see what you think.'

I wasn't really into things like this, but I had a quick read up on it, it seemed okay.

'Stick it on, then. I'll just top my glass up; do you want one?' I asked.

'No, I'm alright now. You go ahead and have the last bit.'

I got my drink and snuggled down to watch the TV; we watched three episodes, which I did enjoy. There was quite a bit of sex in it, none of us said anything whilst watching it, sex wasn't ever a topic we talked about these days. Sebastian seemed to get embarrassed if I brought the subject up, then I would get embarrassed because he was embarrassed, so I never mentioned it. Things were very different than when we were younger. We never talked about how to please each other; it was straight sex, no foreplay. It had been about two and half weeks since we last had sex, and we hadn't mentioned it apart from the day before.

I thought back to when we were younger; things were different then. I would dress up in sexy underwear; we were a bit more experimental. We never asked what we liked or didn't like, though, it just happened. I did wonder whether we had grown apart the last few years or whether Sebastian still fancied me like he did. It's not like we had to stay together for the children. Were we in a rut?

I didn't know the answer. My mind wondered too much sometimes.

About 9.00 pm, I started to think about work the next day. My heart started racing away. After the announcement from Boris on Friday, I didn't know how Joe was going react. I felt myself getting anxious thinking about it.

'Do you want another episode, Charlie?' Sebastian asked.

'No, I'm going to bed, not like some, I have work tomorrow.'

'Now, now, no need to be like that,' Sebastian replied.

'Just saying,' I replied as I walked off to go to bed.

That night, I hardly slept. My mind was in overdrive again, and my tummy was churning. The thought of work and what was going to happen, what about Sebastian not working? Would we financially be okay? Would the kids be okay?

CHAPTER 9

MONDAY
23ᴿᴰ MARCH 2020

Monday morning came around so quick, where did the weekend go? This Monday was different. Sebastian was now at home not working, and I was working from home. We were not used to being around each other so much. It will be interesting times!

We got up the same time as usual and did our morning walk.

At 9.00 am, I dialled into the meeting with Joe and James, both were already on the call.

'Charlie, did you hear the announcement of Friday about the government paying eighty percent of employees' wages if they couldn't work from home?' Joe asked.

'I heard the announcement but haven't seen any information on it yet.'

'Apparently, you can furlough staff,' Joe replied.

Furlough, I thought, what the effing hell does furlough mean? Rather than look stupid, I did a quick search on the internet; it meant leave of absence. For god's sake, why didn't the government use bloody simple words instead of all this fancy lingo! It was bad enough trying to get through this as a business without having to interpret what they were talking about.

'This will make a massive difference to our cash flow, Charlie. Can you find out more about the scheme and what we need to do? We'll have another meeting at 3.00 pm to discuss.'

'Ok, I'll hang off and get on with this,' I replied.

I had a headache already; my day hadn't even started. There was nothing on the government website except a note to say details of the scheme would be out shortly. I called around a few other finance people I knew who work in other businesses. They were as flummoxed as me; nobody seemed to know anything except what had been announced. This was a crystal ball job, I thought. Typical to announce something so critical without the details.

I spoke to HR. They were as blank as me; not the best start to the week. I felt one of those weeks coming on! In the end, I called our accountants who did our audit to see if they could help. They were as useful as they could be. Apparently, the government was going to cover all employees' wages up to eighty percent to a maximum of £2,500 per month. The company had to pay the wages up front but could then claim it back from HMRC once they had a system set up.

Our accountants did the payroll for us so that would be their problem to sort. At least I had some information to give back to Joe. I don't know why I didn't go to our accountants in the first place.

I sent an email to my team to say I wouldn't be joining our meeting today and to go ahead without me. I felt guilty, but I had too much to be getting on with.

Sebastian was very quiet, so I thought I'd check to see what he was up to. I could hear the TV in the lounge.

'Are you okay?' I asked.

'Yep, just watching some TV. Got nothing else to do.'

'Why don't you go shopping while I'm working and get the food,' I suggested.

'I don't feel like it, and anyway, I don't know what we need,' he replied.

'I'll write a list.'

'We'll go later when you've finished work. You're better at things like this than me,' he replied.

'Well, why don't you run the hoover round to help me out?'

'Charlie, why don't you just leave me be. I want to watch TV and be on my own while you're working,' he shouted.

'Okay, I only asked.' I shut the lounge door and went back to the office.

This was going to be a load of fun if he was going to be like this every day. He would have to find an outlet doing something, else we'd end up divorced. I stayed in the office out the way the rest of the day.

Before I knew, it was 3.00 pm and time for another call with Joe.

'Charlie, what have you found out about this furlough scheme?'

'Well, I manged to get some information from our accountants. Apparently, we can lay all the staff off who have been impacted from Covid-19 and can't work from home. The max is eighty percent of an employee's wages up to a maximum of £2,500 per month. I don't know how we claim it back. HMRC is working on a system that will be available in the next few weeks.'

'Well, that would cover all of our staff, wouldn't it?' Joe asked.

James replied, 'I guess so. The installation team definitely can't work, and we would have to question the sales team. I don't think they can carry on their sales duties while all this is going on.'

'So, can we claim this for March payroll, Charlie?' Joe asked.

'I'm guessing it's from a certain date in March. We'll have to then decide going forward, if we decide to go ahead with this, whether we only pay eighty percent of employees' wages or we bear the other twenty percent as a cost?' I replied.

Joe sharply answered,'It doesn't look like we'll have much revenue coming in so the cash flow will be tight. We can only afford to pay the eighty percent. At least we know we can recover that, and let's hope we see this through to the other end.'

Joe continued, 'Charlie, let's start the process on furloughing employees. You'll have to liaise with HR and our accountants on advice on how we go about the process. I also need you to build this into the cash flow so we can look at the next few months and the impact.'

I asked, 'What employees are we looking at, Joe?'

'Everyone, we can't afford to pay them,' he responded.

'Even finance and management?' I asked

'I said everyone; what's the point in having management with no team?' he answered.

'That's fine as long as I understand.'

I ended the call. All sorts of thoughts were going through my head. Am I to be furloughed? Why would I be any different to anyone else?

This was like a living nightmare; I couldn't imagine the government paying nearly all the Uk's wages.

I arranged a team meeting between HR, our accountants, and myself for later that day. The meeting went as well as could. Our accountants advised HR on the letters they needed to send to employees and how the process would work. By the time we had finished the meeting, it was the end of the day.

I logged off and went into the lounge to Sebastian. He was lying on one of the sofa with the news on; there were also a few bottles of empty beers on the table.

'You've missed it,' Sebastian piped up.

'Missed what?'

'The latest Boris announcement.'

'What did he say?'

'Well, if you watch now, it's going to be repeated.' I sat down to watch the news.

The news reader on sky announced, 'The prime minister announces a nationwide lockdown—a drastic set of measures restrict movement and assembly. It is announced that police will be granted powers within days to enforce the government's "social distancing" measures.

The public is supposed to stay at home and only leave for list of reasonable excuses.

'It comes following reports of many people flouted its advice on "social distancing"—staying home as much as possible to curb the spread of the virus.

'The government also asks about 1.5million vulnerable people who will likely need hospital treatment to "shield" themselves. This involves voluntarily staying at home for twelve weeks to avoid getting the virus.'

Wow, this was, in fact, the law now, I thought. This made everything sound official. Our freedom had legally gone; we could no longer do what we wanted. I looked at Sebastian, he was half cut.

'We need to do some shopping.'

'Yep, if that's what you want to do. I've been waiting for you all day.'

'I've had to work; you know that. I haven't had the chance to lay around all day watching TV and drinking,' I snapped.

'Good old you, just carry on with your work,' he replied.

'Just F off,' I replied angrily.

I was so angry with Sebastian. He was in a depressive mode. I decided to go shopping on my own and not have him round me in this state.

I eventually got to the supermarket at Tesco, and oh my god, I couldn't believe the queues. Was this real? The queue was all around the car park. There must have been about thirty people in front of me. There were yellow markings on the ground to maintain safe distancing, and most people were wearing masks. Was this the real normal?

I ended up queueing for about twenty-five minutes; eventually, I got to the front. The bouncer on the door explained to me how it worked.

'When you go in, madam, it's a one-way system. You must follow the arrows and keep to the distance of the arrows. You will then queue for a till, and staff will guide you to a till to pay.'

'Okay, thank you,' I responded as I walked into the store.

This was like something from an alien century. All staff had masks on. I could see that the tills had plastic Perspex up around the cashier; it didn't feel like a normal shop. As I went around the supermarket, things were marked up with the maximum amounts you could purchase, and most items had a max of two items per purchase.

The supermarket was very low on stock, and many items I wanted were out of stock. And guess what? They were out of stock of toilet rolls! I got what I could and headed for the checkout.

Well, my first shop during lockdown was a bit of a shock. I never thought for one minute that it would be like this. Gemma was right to stock up. I never imagined it would be like this.

When I returned home, Sebastian was asleep on the sofa. I didn't bother to wake him. I put the shopping away and went to bed. I couldn't be bothered to eat; it had been a busy day, and I was feeling tired.

CHAPTER 10
TUESDAY 24TH MARCH 2020

I slept well tonight. I hadn't slept well for the last few nights, and it had caught up with me. I woke up about 5.45 am just before the alarm. Sebastian was in bed; I don't know what time he came up.

I got up before the alarm went off and went downstairs to make myself a drink. I heard the alarm go off. Sebastian turned it off. I couldn't hear him getting up, so I decided to go for a walk on my own.

When I got back, Sebastian was in the kitchen.

'Did you get any yoghurt?'

'Sorry, I missed the yoghurt.'

He started tutting.

'Well, if you could be arsed and not so pissed maybe you would have come with me. I'm the one who stood in a queue for twenty minutes before even getting into the supermarket after a day's work. So don't stand there dictating to me about f'cking yoghurt.'

'Sorry for interrupting your busy social life to go shopping.'

'Why don't you p*** off, Sebastian; get a life,' I shouted.

I walked off so angry. What had got into him? Why couldn't he be grateful that I went shopping? He always had to pick fault with something.

I had a shower and got myself ready in the office for my call.

I had trouble dialling into the call today. It was the internet connection, probably because every man and his dog were working from home. I'm not an IT expert, so what did I know?

Eventually, I got on the team meeting.

'Better late than never, Charlie,' Joe said.

I felt like commenting with a F word but held myself back. Right now, with everything going on at home and the coronavirus, I could easily tell him to stick his job. The job and Joe made me felt so uptight and irritable.

'Our accountants are working with HR to send out the relevant documents to employees. I'm hoping this will be done in the next day or two,' I said.

'Good,' Joe said. 'I now need you to move back as many payments as you can. The PAYE, VAT, rent, etc., then update a final cash flow.'

'Yes, okay, I'll see what I can do,' I replied.

That day, I negotiated with creditors where I could, the landlord, the council and HMRC to stop PAYE and VAT payments. Most calls I spent two hours on the phone queueing to talk to someone.

By the end of the day, I felt shattered, doing things like this was no fun; most businesses were in the same position.

The thought of everyone being furloughed by the end of the week was frightening. I wondered what employees would think? Could they manage on eighty percent of their wages? Some may enjoy not working and getting eighty percent of their pay, I thought. And how about us? I could not help but do some sums on my calculator. I scribbled on a piece of paper how much I would earn at eighty percent. I kept Sebastian's salary at nil for now and listed all the outgoings we had. We could just manage if we didn't spend on anything else, what else was there to spend anything on, we were in a lockdown, and everything was shut.

I hadn't spoken to Sebastian since the morning; it was best we stayed out of each other's way. I wasn't particularly impressed with his attitude.

It was 5.00 pm, the day had gone so fast. Even though I was exhausted I thought it best to update the cash flow with all the changes of the furlough scheme and payments I had delayed. It took until about 7.00 pm to get everything finished and log off.

I heard the TV on in the lounge. The door was shut. I decided to go straight upstairs and have a hot bath. I was sure if I'd gone into the lounge there would be more confrontation. I couldn't smell anything cooking either. I guess Sebastian hadn't bothered cooking anything for dinner. I hadn't eaten all day, just cups of tea and water to keep me going. No wonder I felt exhausted.

It was lovely to lie in a hot soapy bath. I lit some candles to help me relax. It was only Tuesday, but it felt like a Friday already. My period had finished, my tummy had started to feel much better, however, my whole body still felt achy; the joints in my arms and legs hurt. Maybe I'm coming down with something, I thought. I hoped the hot bath would help.

After my bath, I put on some cosy pyjamas, and that was it for the night. I went downstairs in hope things were better with Sebastian than the morning.

I opened the lounge door where Sebastian was lying on the sofa watching the TV.

'You've worked late today,' he said.

'Yes, I've been working through this furlough scheme.'

'Furlough scheme? What's that mean?' Sebastian asked.

I laughed. 'That's what I thought; it's some posh word the government has come up with. It's basically the eighty percent of wages the government is going to pay to employees who can't work during this lockdown.'

'Oh, right; no mention on what they're doing for the self-employed yet?' he asked.

'I haven't heard anything, Sebastian.'

He sat up and stared out of the window. He looked dreadful; he hadn't had a shave, and I'm sure he hadn't eaten at all.

'Shall I do some food?' I asked.

'It's late. I've got some chicken in the fridge. I might just have that in a wrap,' he replied.

'Okay, I'll do it.'

Sebastian asked, 'What are you going to have?'

'I might just have some tuna salad.'

I went off to the kitchen to prepare our food' it didn't take long to do. It was a cold meal for us. Sebastian came into the kitchen and sat at the table.

'That tuna salad looks nice,' he commented.

'Yea, something simple. I'm still watching the calories. Do you want some?'

'No, I'm fine, thanks, happy with a wrap. I don't know why you're watching the calories; I've told you before, you don't eat enough, and that's why your weight is like a yoyo up and down.'

'Why do you always revert back to my weight?' I yelled.

I was sure Sebastian enjoyed upsetting me and putting me down. I was at a point where I thought he did it without realising, either that or he got a kick out it.

'I've done lots of nutritional plans for you and you never stick to them,' he said.

'I do try them, but I find there's too much food in them. I'd be a right bloater if I ate that amount of food.'

'That's my point when I say you don't eat enough, so your body eats into your reserves.'

Sebastian talked to me as if I was one of his clients. He'd have me doing press ups next, I thought.

'Look, if you don't like what I look like go and find someone else.'

'Where's that come from? Of course, I like you as you are. You are the one who seems to be unhappy with your weight. I'm only trying to give you some advice,' Sebastian sighed.

'Do you mind if we drop the subject? I want to just eat my meal.'

'Hmmm, yes, of course.' Sebastian tucked into his wrap.

I stood and leaned back against the kitchen cupboard whilst tucking into my salad.

'What have you been up today?' I asked.

'Nothing much, browsed the internet, still can't find anywhere to get any weights anytime soon, and I read up on a few nutritional articles. Brushing up on knowledge I'd say.' He laughed.

'Oh, nice, glad you've kept busy today.'

'There's nothing on TV tonight; it's all depressing with the news on the coronavirus. Italy and Spain seem to be in a bad way. Do you want to watch another episode of Narcos? Sebastian asked.

'Yes, might as well; it's better than getting even more depressed watching the news.'

We managed to keep our eyes open to watch one episode of Narcos before bed. Bed was another story. We have a super king-sized bed; I sleep on the edge of one side, and Sebastian sleeps on the edge of the other side; it's like being in separate beds. We couldn't be any farther apart. We might join in the middle once a week for sex, not even once a week lately.

Tonight was no different to any other night. We said goodnight and snuggled down in the quilt on our separate sides of the bed. As usual, I had difficulty getting off to sleep, then awoke around 2.00 am with hot flushes. This was a nightly theme of late.

CHAPTER 11

WEDNESDAY 25ᵀᴴ MARCH 2020

Wednesday was much of a muchness. I managed to get an early morning walk in before work. Sebastian was still asleep in bed, so I let him be; after all, he had nothing much to get up early for.

I skipped breakfast. I didn't fancy much to eat, and there's no point eating if you are not hungry!

I logged on ready for my call at 9.00 am. For some reason, today my computer wouldn't connect to the VPN. I switched the router off and back on again. It took about ten minutes for the router to reboot. It was now 9.10 am, and I still hadn't connected.

My mobile pinged; it was a text from Joe. 'Are you up? Are you joining the call?'

He was being sarcastic. I messaged back, 'Having trouble with the VPN.'

I tried to reboot the router again. It was a right pain in the backside. The router was on a shelf below the telephone in the office, so to get to it, you had to get on your hands and knees. I felt myself getting stressed and flustered.

'Why won't this bloody thing work?' I said to myself.

I was up and down from the desk to the floor trying to sort out the router. I felt my face getting redder and redder, and my body was getting hotter and hotter. I couldn't breathe properly; this was all I needed was a hot sweat. I got up off the floor, rolled up my sleeves, and opened the window to let some air in.

I knelt one more time to the router to see if the green light had come on. It was still flashing orange. I yanked the router off the shelf, and in doing so, it pulled the wires, and the telephone dropped on to the floor.

'For god's sake,' I shouted. My patience was running short. I don't have much patience these days with anything. I picked the phone up off the floor; all the wires were tangled between the phone and the router.

'Who's been messing with this and left it like this,' I said quite loudly. On that my mobile pinged again. 'Have you fixed it yet?' Joe texted. What was wrong with this guy? If I'd fixed it, I'd be on the call. I reached up for my phone on the desk and sat on the floor to text back, 'No, not fixed. We'll have to do the meeting later.'

I took a deep breath to calm myself. I wiped my face on my sleeve. I could feel myself burning up. I reached back towards the desk and threw my mobile back on to the desk with angrily force. I didn't aim very well, and my mobile bounced off the side of the desk and onto to the wooden floor.

I slid myself along the floor to reach for my mobile. As I picked it up, I could see that the screen on the front of my mobile had cracked. I couldn't believe it. Bloody marvellous. I had never dropped a mobile in my life; the minute we go into lockdown and shops are closed, I drop the phone. You couldn't make this up!

I know started talking out loud to myself. 'What is it with men? Why does Joe have to keep texting me when I said I couldn't connect? I shouldn't have to use my personal phone for work? Sick of this house and this job.'

On that, Sebastian popped his head around the office door.

'Oh, I didn't hear you get up?' I said.

'What's all the noise in here? What are you doing on the floor?' he asked.

'Errr, the internet won't connect and look how all the wires are tangled,' I shouted.

'Wow, calm down; you look like you're going to have a coronary arrest. Your face is all red.'

'You don't say clever clogs. I tell you what, you sit down here and sort it all out. I'm sick of sorting other people's problems out. I haven't tangled all these wires.'

'Neither have I,' Sebastian shouted back.

'Oh, it must be the ghost of the Dyson household,' I said.

'You're pathetic sometimes; it's never your fault, is it?'

Sebastian looked over on the desk. 'And what have you done to your mobile?'

'I threw it up the wall in temper.'

'What on earth has got into you? Why did you do that?' he asked.

God, this guy is a complete idiot if he believes I threw my mobile up the wall. I nodded my head at him with disgust that he believed what I said.

'Come out the way. I'll have a look at the Wi-Fi.'

Sebastian handed out his arm for me to hold onto to pull myself off the floor.

'Go wash your face. You look like you've got yourself in a state,' he said.

'I look a state? Look at you. No top on, your hair is everywhere, and you need a shave,' I sharply replied.

'I'm not going to respond, Charlie. You're off your head sometimes. I'm only trying to help you. I've just gotten up, give me a break.'

I went off into the kitchen and made a cup of tea, leaving Sebastian in the office to sort out the internet. I looked in the mirror. My face was blood red. I was so hot and bothered. I made Sebastian a cup of tea and left it on the kitchen table. He appeared in the kitchen about ten minutes later.

'I've sorted it.'

'Is it working?'

'Yes, I just said it's sorted, didn't I?'

'Oh, okay. I'll go and see if I can log on.'

As I walked off, Sebastian shouted to me, 'A thank you wouldn't go amiss.'

'Thanks,' I shouted back.

I sat at the desk and logged on, praying the VPN would connect; the VPN didn't work.

I called, 'Sebastian, it's still not working. I thought you'd fixed it?'

I heard him say, 'For goodness sake' as he marched back into the office.

He checked the router and then had a look at my laptop.

'Charlie, the internet is working. It must be a problem with the VPN connection. I'll go get the iPad to check our internet.'

He walked off upstairs to get the iPad. Shortly after, he shouted, 'Yep, the internet is working so it's not us.'

I was getting really frustrated now and shouted, 'What is it then?'

As Sebastian walked back downstairs to the office, he said, 'I don't know, Charlie. I think it's something to do with your work connection; it's not our end. You'll have to ring your IT department to help you.'

Bloody great help that was. It was now 10.30 am, and I hadn't started work, and to top it, I had a smashed mobile. And I wondered why my blood pressure felt high? I could have exploded right now.

Our IT was outsourced, so this would be an interesting conversation. I found the number and gave them a call. To top it all, I had to go through a series of options. I could hardly see my screen on my mobile to press the buttons. Why was everything so difficult? Eventually, I got through and explained the problem.

This IT tech pipes up, 'I can see the problem; your password has expired.'

I thought is this guy having a laugh. All this palaver this morning, and he's telling me it's my password.

'I'll reset it for you, Charlotte, and give you the new password. Once you login, it is best that you change the new password to something you are familiar with.'

'Thank you,' I said with relief.

Eventually, at 10.45 am, I got on the system. What a morning. I hoped the rest of the day was better than this. On that, Sebastian brought me a cup of tea into the office.

'Got it sorted?' he asked

'Yes, it was my password.'

Sebastian didn't comment. I noticed he still wasn't dressed or had a shave; I didn't comment as I needed to get on with my work.

'Thanks for the tea,' I called as he walked off back to the kitchen.

I checked my emails and noticed Joe had moved the meeting to 2.00 pm. That was fine; it gave me a bit longer to check some of the numbers in the cash flow.

I called Summer to see if she knew anybody who repaired phones. She didn't while the lockdown was going on, but she took the opportunity to remind me how mad I was when she was younger and dropped her phone. It's funny it being on the other shoe. I felt like the naughty child now. Summer seemed okay and was enjoying her day off doing some gardening. I was due an upgrade in a couple of months. I would have to make do with my mobile until then.

I finished the changes to the cash flow around 1.30 pm. That's it, I thought; all done. I clicked on save and unbelievably the file wouldn't save. This was the icing on the cake. I had a meeting in thirty minutes, and the stupid file wouldn't save. I kept getting an error message saying the file was too big.

I shouted, 'I'm going to throw this laptop through the window. I've had enough now.'

I pushed the laptop to one side with my right hand and put my head back in the chair. Joe would think I was making all of this up.

Sebastian appeared. 'What's the shouting about now?'

'Oh, my file won't save; it's saying there's not enough disk space. I've got a meeting with Joe in fifteen minutes. He'll never believe me.'

Sebastian suggested, 'There's a Toshiba portable hard drive on the bookshelf. Why don't you save to that?'

I looked over at the bookcase. 'I never thought of that. I'll try it.'

'Do you want any lunch?' he asked.

'Naaa, I need to get on.'

He still wasn't dressed or shaven. What was wrong with him? I thought. What was he doing all day? I hadn't got time to get into a conversation with him now. I grabbed the hard drive and plugged into the laptop. I clicked on save and prayed that it saved. Luckily. it did. I emailed it across to Joe and joined the call.

'Having fun?' Joe said.

'I'm about to throw this f'cking laptop through the window.' I responded.

'Blimey, Charlie, it's not that bad.'

'You've not had the day I've had.'

'Clearly not; you need to take a chill pill,' Joe said.

'Can we just get on with the meeting. I've got a million and one things to be getting on with.'

'Sure, Charlie. Is there anything we can do to help you?' Joe asked.

I responded with one word 'no'. I was still angry over my mobile phone; if he hadn't been pestering with stupid texts, I wouldn't have smashed it.

I spent the next fifteen minutes talking through the financial model. Everything seemed to stack up now that we could furlough the staff. For the last fifteen minutes, the HR manager joined. She talked through the process for furloughing staff and where they were up to. We planned for all staff to be furloughed from Friday. I had passed caring by this stage. I wanted to see the end of the day.

After the call, I finished off some other bits of work, then logged off. I felt absolutely drained. I don't know why I let myself get into these states. I'll give myself a heart attack one of these days.

I had a hot bath, then chilled with another episode of Narco's. I'd got into the series—unusual for me to enjoy a drug cartel series; must be all the sex in it that made it interesting. I had not had anything to eat all day. Sebastian prepared a pasta salad for us to eat while we watched TV. Sebastian still hadn't shaven. I'm not even sure he got dressed today. I chose not to ask or ask about what he'd been up to. Sounds selfish, but I wanted to chill after a mad day and didn't have the energy to listen to other people's problems. That sounds bad, he's my husband not just anybody! I should rephase that. I couldn't deal with other problems today.

I fell asleep on the sofa watching TV. Sebastian woke me for bed around 10.00 pm. As soon as my head hit the pillow, I zonked out. I was in the need of a good sleep.

CHAPTER 12
THURSDAY 26TH MARCH 2020

I woke up at 6.00 am. This was late for me. Sebastian was on his side of the bed snoring his head off. The rain was bouncing off the floor outside, no walk today, I thought.

It was Thursday, past halfway through the week, and things couldn't be as bad as yesterday.

As usual this week, I was up and ready for work in no time. I left Sebastian in bed to sleep; no point him getting up to early.

I logged on for the call at 9.00 am; this time, HR were invited for the full meeting. HR gave a full update on the progress of furloughing staff.

I asked, 'I assume all my finance team is included in this?'

She replied, 'Yes, Charlie, it's all staff.'

I wanted to ask if this included myself, but I didn't have the guts on the call. One thing I did know, all my staff would no longer be working after Friday, or any staff at all. I had focused so much over the past week on the cash flow and government initiatives that I hadn't really thought about the event of myself being furloughed. I'd done a quick calculation of our financial commitments, but that was it.

I had a team call with my staff later that morning. My thoughts were to postpone it until tomorrow. I may have too many questions today that I couldn't answer. I needed an easier day compared to yesterday. After deep thought, I cancelled the meeting.

Joe called me about 11.00 am.

'Charlie, can you give me a list of all outstanding suppliers?'

'Sure, I'll send an aged creditor listing across.'

I emailed an aged creditor summary across. Joe reviewed it, instructing me to schedule or make certain payments. Apart from that, Thursday was quiet, nothing like Wednesday.

Mitch called me about 3.00 pm.

'Hi, Mom, how are you?'

'I'm good, son. Had a bit of a wobble yesterday with IT issues, but okay today. I have dropped my mobile, so the screen is all cracked. I can't see much of it.'

'Dear me, Mother, if that were Summer or I you would be going mad when we were younger.'

I laughed. 'I know; it was an accident. It fell off the desk on the office.'

'Ours was an accident.' Mitch laughed

'Anyway, I'll get it sorted. Luckily, I'm due an upgrade in a few weeks. I'll get you or Summer to look at it nearer the time. I'm no good with phones.'

'No problem, Mom, how's Dad doing with the gyms closed?'

'To be honest, Mitch, he's not that good. He's not getting dressed or shaving, and he's lost without the gym. You know your dad, he usually gets up, showers, and has a shave. I haven't had much time to speak with him with the work load I have.'

'Just keep an eye on him, Mom. I bet he feels he's lost his livelihood.'

'I will do, son; how are things with you?'

'Yea, busy, a new coronavirus loan has been introduced called CBIL's to support businesses, but we don't have all the full details yet. They keep changing the process, and it's frustrating for clients.'

'I bet Joe might be interested in that. I'll mention it on the call tomorrow.'

'Look, Mom. I had better get on. Both of you take care. Love you lots. I'll call you the weekend.'

'Love you lots too, Mitch. Take care of yourself and stay safe,' I replied.

The rest of Thursday seemed to go smooth with no hassle. I worked in the office all day, and I didn't see or hear from Sebastian once. I didn't stop for lunch so there was no need to leave the office.

Around 5.00 pm, I logged off and went to see what Sebastian was up to. Again, he was slobbed on the sofa not dressed or shaven. I'm not used to seeing him like this. Usually, he was working out and keeping fit. There were also a few empty beer bottles on the lounge table again; not working was depressing him.

I had a hot bath as usual then came downstairs. Sebastian was asleep on the sofa.

I shook him. 'Do you want anything to eat?'

He looked at me and replied, 'Oh, my wife is back; not seen you all day.'

I ignored the comment and went into the kitchen. I decided to cook spaghetti Bolognaise, quick and easy. I had the tomato sauce, and the spaghetti wouldn't take too long. I hadn't eaten all day; I was starving and in need for some carbs!

Sebastian followed me into the kitchen.

'How's lovely Joe today?' he asked.

'What are you talking about, Sebastian?'

'You seem to care more about pleasing Joe than me,' Sebastian slurred.

'You're drunk and talking rubbish.'

Sebastian grabbed my arm. 'Do you think I don't know?'

I yelled, 'Let go of my arm.'

He walked off back into the lounge.

All the time Sebastian and I had been together, he had never grabbed my arm like that. Why on earth would he think there was something going on between Joe and me?

I opened a bottle of prosecco and drank a glass straight back while finishing cooking the meal.

I shouted, 'Do you want some of this spaghetti Bolognese?'

Sebastian shouted back, 'I might have some in a bit.'

I sat in the kitchen and ate my meal. I still couldn't believe he thought there was something between Joe and me. What has happened to us? I thought. Why on earth would Sebastian think that? He has never grabbed my arm like that before. Have we grown apart?

I went off to bed and didn't bother going back in the lounge where Sebastian was; it was best to give him some space. I took a glass of prosecco up to bed and did some surfing on the iPad in bed.

Around 11.00 pm, I heard Sebastian coming up the stairs. I lay still and pretended to be asleep. He took off his sleep shorts and got into bed without saying anything. Within minutes, he was fast asleep.

I lay awake for ages thinking of what happened. I had never seen Sebastian like this. Usually, he dressed very smart, a bit of a lady's man, I would say. He took very good care of his body and was always clean shaven. Surely, he could not be depressed after being home a few days, I thought. I started to question whether there was something deeper with our marriage? My mind was in overdrive again. I needed to switch off, else I would end up going mad. Maybe I was already mad?

Eventually, I fell into a deep sleep. I slept till around 5.00 am; that was good going for me.

Chapter 13

Friday 27th March 2020

I looked at my mobile, Friday 27th March 2020 at 5.00 am. It was Friday! Thank goodness. I got up and put on the news. I hadn't listened to the news for a few days.

Apparently, it was announced the night before.

'The police's new enforcement powers come into effect following Johnson's announcement of a nationwide lockdown on 23 March.

'People are no longer allowed to leave their home without reasonable excuse. This is, in effect, a form of house arrest. It means that we are only supposed to leave our homes for limited reasons. The four most common reasons are:

Shopping for necessities like food and medicine
Taking exercise—but only once a day
For medical reasons, to provide care or help to vulnerable persons
For essential work, and non-essential work when working from home is not possible.

Also banned are public gatherings of more than two people—with those found in breach facing a fine of £30 in the first instance. There are even fewer permitted reasons to gather than there are to leave your house.'

I felt the anxiety coming on again after listening to that; it highlighted this was a serious matter now for the UK. I wondered when I would get to see the kids again. And goodness knows how Sebastian was going to get on? He was already falling apart.

Boris didn't look well when I watched the announcement, but I suppose he had a lot of weight on his shoulders. This was an unprecedented time, who knows what decisions to make.

One hundred and eighty-one deaths were reported today from the virus, the biggest increase yet in the UK. I felt so much for all those people and their families. My heart went out to everyone and all our NHS workers. I started to think of Summer working in that environment, and tears started to run down my face. I wished my parents were still alive to give me a big hug right now. I eventually switched the news off and wiped dry my eyes.

I decided to go for a walk; the only walk I could do according to guidelines, to clear my head. It was very quiet everywhere today, not much traffic on the road; it was like a ghost town.

When I got back, Sebastian was still in bed, so I logged on to get on with some work. We had the normal call at 9.00 am. The call only lasted about ten minutes; Joe didn't say much. At the end of the call, Joe asked, 'Charlie, can I have a separate call with you at 10 am please, and James, can I have a call with you at 11.00 am.'

'Yes, sure,' I said. James also agreed.

I wondered why he wanted a separate call. May be he wanted more scenario's modelling. Sebastian was still in bed. I made my self some breakfast today, just cereal. It was Friday, and I was so looking forward to the weekend break. By the time I had my breakfast, it was nearly 10.00 am. Still no sign of Sebastian. I joined on to the team call a few minutes early and waited for Joe to join.

'Thank you so much, Charlie, for all of the hard work you have put in over the last few days,' Joe said.

'That's okay, Joe.'

'Well, I don't know to say this, but we are going to have to furlough you too,' Joe muttered.

It went silent for a few moments. I should have guessed this was coming. Why would I be any different than anyone else?

Joe explained, 'I have to do what's best for the interests of the business, Charlie. You are being treated the same as all other management. I am going to have the same conversation with James after you. It is the best chance I have of saving the business. You'll still receive eighty percent of your pay until this is over.'

'No need to explain, Joe. I understand. Why should I be treated any differently?'

I felt myself filling up with tears; it had been an emotional week, and this felt like an ending to an era—every man to fight for themselves.

'Charlie, I hope you and your family keep safe. As soon as we are through this and can operate again normally, we will return to work,' Joe said.

'It's fine, Joe. I'm sure that will be soon.'

'I hope so, Charlie. Thank you again for everything you've done. Listen, don't work late today; get yourself off and enjoy the weekend best you can.'

'Thanks, Joe, hopefully speak to you soon.'

I hung off feeling completely numb. I started to cry; everything felt so over whelming. It felt like the end of the world as if I was in a dream and none of this was happening.

I had to pull myself together as I had a call with my team at 11.00 am; it was also their last day.

I logged on to the call, and the three were chatting away. It felt so strange; we all talked and shared some tears. We all hoped that we got through this and be there at the other end. In reality, none of us knew what was going to happen, and the apprehension was frightening.

Never in my career did I hope to see anything like this again. It was the unknown, not knowing how long this was going to go on and whether we could survive.

On top of work, it was the stress of Sebastian not earning any money. We still had a mortgage and bills to pay. Would we manage? I kept thinking.

Sebastian got up about lunch time; I had never known him stay in bed so late.

'Everything okay?' he asked.

I started to cry. He put his arms around me 'What's the matter, hun?'

I told him about work and that I'd been furloughed. He held me tight and kissed me on the head.

'Will we be okay?' I asked Sebastian

'As long as we have each other, and we are healthy, that's the main thing.'

This was it now; we were in lockdown together, just the two of us. I hoped our marriage survived this. We'd had our moments over the last week or so, but it had been really stressful with everything we'd had to deal with, probably no different to other families. I believe we'd both felt like killing each other over the past few days.

Sebastian and I had been together from a young age. I had no idea what would happen if something happened to one of us. I know you seem to plod along in a routine as you get older; it's not like jumping into bed together every five minutes when you're younger, but the love is still the same if not stronger.

'I'll cook us a lovely meal, babe, tonight and we'll work it out.'

I wiped my eyes and snivelled. 'Yea, that would be nice.'

'I'll cook your favourite meal, cheese and potato pie with spareribs.'

I smiled. Sebastian pinched my chin. 'That's my girl.'

I went upstairs and washed my face. I felt like there was a big hole in my life not working. I wondered whether I would ever see people again. I could understand now how Sebastian had felt all week. It was a big change to take in and then there was the not being to go anywhere or see anybody. It was like being a prisoner in your own home.

I thought of all those people who were on their own and the vulnerable. It must be devastating for them not even being able to even go food shopping.

I switched my laptop off at 4.00 pm. I hadn't received anymore emails, and I didn't suppose I would for a while. Joe said to just check periodically for updates.

Sebastian cooked the lovely meal he promised, and we sat at the table to eat.

'Well, my lovely, we have each other and let's make the most of what we have.'

Sebastian opened a bottle of prosecco and poured us a glass.

I held my glass up. 'Yes, I'll drink to that; let's pray we get through this.'

'We will, hun; we'll look after each other. I'm so proud of our children and how they are working so hard through lockdown.'

'Me too, Sebastian, they are good kids; we've brought them up well and they have good work morals. I hope they are both okay through this.'

'They will be, my dear. They are both very strong individuals. We need to keep strong too.'

We finished off our meals and washed up. It was nice and early to tonight, not as late as previous nights with all the stress of work.

'Do you want to watch another Narco's episode? Sebastian smiled.

'It's not a bad series to be fair. We might get two episodes in tonight. It's not as if I've got to get up in the morning for work.'

'Come on, let's relax,' Sebastian said as he topped our glasses up with prosecco. He grabbed my hand and pulled me into the lounge behind him.

'You still haven't had a shave since you finished work.'

'I wondered how long before you made a comment again.' He laughed

'I don't like beards, and it doesn't suit you. You look like Father Christmas; it's a bit grey.'

Sebastian laughed. 'I'll have a shave in the morning, just for you if it makes you happy.'

I smiled and sat on the sofa ready to watch TV. We watched two episodes tonight and stopped up a little later than usual. By 11.00 pm, I could feel my eyes getting heavy.

'Ready for bed?' Sebastian asked.

'I think so; I've got a bit of a headache, so a good night's sleep won't go amiss.'

No longer had we got in bed and Sebastian was snoring his head off.

I still struggled to get to sleep. I picked my mobile up and texted Summer and Mitch.

'Hi, both; your dad and I are okay. I got furloughed from work today. Hope you are both okay. Love you both very much, and we are very proud of the work you are doing.'

My eyes filled with tears as I wrote the text. We were very proud of them. I feel old when I send messages like this. They were young, having so much to look forward into life. We have to class ourselves as middle aged now. Wow, that is frightening. Where had the time gone! I remembered back to being the same age as Summer. It feels like yesterday. Sebastian and I enjoyed life to the fullest when we were that age.

Summer messaged back almost immediately. 'I'm sorry, Mom. At least you and dad can spend some quality time together for once. Think of us poor workers still having to work. Lol.'

Mitch also joined in the conversation. 'Enjoy it, Mom. Never again will the government pay your wages to be at home. I know what I'd rather be doing.'

They were lovely, reassuring messages. Reality is, I had not ever spent this amount of time alone with Sebastian for a long time. We had both always worked. It was a bit scary as to how we would get on.

Only time would tell.

Was this make or break?

Would we get on together?

I didn't sleep well that night. I had all these questions going through my head. The first thing I thought is that in the morning we must go through all our expenses to make sure we are okay. I'd done a quick calculation, but I needed to do a more detailed analysis. I think this is the accountancy coming out of me. I have to balance everything to the penny and analyse everything.

As usual, I woke with hot sweats about 2.30 am. I got up and washed my face in the bathroom. I couldn't help but think that it had been three weeks since we last had sex. I know we haven't particularity been close as late, but was this normal for a couple of our age or was there something wrong with us?

I'd always felt in control of my life, but for this once, I didn't. The thought of being locked down for the foreseeable future with just the two of us and only one walk a day. I thought about couples who didn't get on. How would they cope? How about people in domestic violence relationships?

The thought of all these possibilities made me emotional. Again, I felt tears rolling down my face. I got very emotional these days over nothing specific. One thing I had to be positive about, Sebastian had never hit me or give me emotional abuse. No woman deserves that. I was lucky in that sense.

I looked over at Sebastian, who was sleeping like a baby. I touched him on the head, followed by a kiss on the head; he was in a deep sleep. I held his hand and snuggled down in the quilt. Tomorrow or should I say today, it was after midnight, was another day. It was going to be a new chapter in our life, one we had never experienced before!

CHAPTER 14

APRIL 2020

So, this was it, Saturday 28th March 2020, our first day together not working and locked inside. It probably wouldn't feel much different as it was the weekend, most likely Monday morning it would hit us.

The weekend went well. We kept busy. There were lots of jobs in the house to catch up on. We did some weeding in the garden, tidied the garage, and stripped all the beds. We both got in the kitchen and cooked some nice meals between us. So far so good; we didn't bicker, and both got on.

The clocks went forward Saturday night. It was lovely Sunday and bright nice and early. It makes you feel much better with the lighter mornings and nights.

Albeit we had a great weekend and didn't argue, we still didn't manage to have sex; this had been almost a month now. I tried to not think of it, but deep inside, I still wondered if this was normal and whether we had a deeper problem with our marriage.

The weekend went so fast, and before we knew it, it was Monday morning. We hadn't set the alarm, and we slept in until 8.00 am. I couldn't believe the time when I woke up. I hadn't slept in this late for a long time. Maybe it's not having the stress of work? I thought.

It felt strange not having to log on to work and join meetings with Joe. I still logged on about 10.30 am to see if I had any emails; there was nothing. I went to Excel and thought it best Sebastian and I did an income and expenditure spreadsheet to make sure we were okay and that we knew what was coming out when. I did the initial spreadsheet, then called Sebastian to look over it and input any things I may have missed.

By the end of it, we agreed we would just be okay without dipping into our savings. I hadn't put any earnings in for Sebastian for the time being as we weren't sure what the self-employed would get.

That was a relief for both of us; it put our minds at rest. I'm sure a lot of people weren't in this position, and I do feel sorry for them.

I spoke to Summer and Mitch today. They thought I was lucky being furloughed and said that I should enjoy the time not working. Both think I work too hard and that it would be good to spend some time with Sebastian. I wasn't totally convinced with their theory, but who knows?

Tuesday was a much of a muchness except I had stomach cramps. I felt as if I was going to come on my period albeit I wasn't due for another couple of weeks. I also felt tired, drained and irritable with my emotions high again. We watched the news in the evening, and it talked about the number of deaths from coronavirus and how we had not reached the peak yet; it really was depressing.

Wednesday was the beginning of a new month, 1st April 2020. Normally, I would play jokes on the family for April Fools, but I felt it wasn't appropriate this year. I remembered once calling Summer to tell her we had won the lottery. She fell for it and thought we had won millions! If only... Another time, I told the kids I was pregnant; again, they fell for it—the good old days.

Instead, I had bad stomach pains, period pains it felt like. I took some paracetamol to help ease the pain. In the afternoon, I felt a bit of a gush in my pants. I went to the toilet to see I was bleeding again. This time, I put a small pad on, thought it best not to use tampons. I knew it wasn't my period but couldn't understand why I had started bleeding or how long it was going to last. I was a little worried as to why I was bleeding again.

The bleeding continued for about another five days; sex wasn't an issue. Sebastian never even asked or tried it on. Goodness knows how long we had gone now without sex; I could be a nun, I thought. The longer it went on, the worse I felt. It was if our marriage had come to an end, and we were only with each other for the sake of it.

One of our neighbours had set up a gym in their garage. They welcomed Sebastian to use the facilities when he wished. Sebastian was overjoyed he could use a gym again. He popped over most days to do a workout. He was back in his element working out, he had started shaving again daily, and didn't appear depressed at all.

I felt not so good through April. The intermittent bleeding was on my mind and the lack of sex between us was also on my mind. I got more depressed as the month went on. I had moments where I couldn't breathe, being honest, I could have done with an inhaler at times. My tummy was very swollen. I looked three months pregnant.

I drank more prosecco than ever from boredom. Sebastian seemed to have got into a routine, and I seemed to be a bit all over the place. The alcohol didn't help; it made me more depressed and often crying most nights. I had never felt so alone and isolated.

Sebastian started running for about an hour each day as well as the gym. I don't know where he got the energy from; he was obsessed with keeping fit. I didn't have the energy to do any of that. I could feel the weight piling on as I drank a bottle of wine or prosecco each night just to get by.

April was a challenging month. Sebastian often criticised me for drinking too much alcohol and being too argumentative. I criticised Sebastian for being a fitness freak and not thinking of his family.

I often felt alone with no one to talk to. Summer and Mitch were very busy with work, and I didn't want to burden them with my stupidity. I missed them so much.

It was still on my mind when Sebastian thought there was something going on between Joe and me. I was horrified at the time. I think I would feel complimented right now, the fact that he thought somebody else would be interested in me. All of that seemed to have changed. Sebastian was enjoying his time, and I was the one probably feeling jealous of how well he was getting on.

On the 5th of April, Boris Johnson was admitted to St Thomas' Hospital in central London for further tests as a "precautionary step", after his coronavirus symptoms persisted. This was a worrying time for us all.

I checked the website for Goa daily to see if there was any change in the status to fly into India. Everything was still the same, not that we could fly from the UK now given we were in a national lockdown. On Saturday 11th April, Sebastian and I decided to unpack our cases. We concluded that we weren't going anywhere, not now or even this year at all I felt. We hadn't even got a holiday to look forward to anymore. I loved travelling and being in the sunshine. I felt like being a prisoner in our own home.

The bleeding stopped completely on the 7th of April, albeit my tummy didn't feel much better. I didn't know whether my next period would be on the Tuesday 14th April when it was officially due or would it be different because I'd been bleeding. God only knows!

On the afternoon of 11th April, after we had unpacked, Sebastian and I had the biggest argument ever; it started over something stupid. I was reading a magazine and it was talking about how many times a couple had sex a week. I read it to Sebastian and made a comment.

'Did you know, in a good relationship couples have sex between two and three times a week? We're obviously not in a good relationship, are we?'

Sebastian completely went off. 'Last time I tried, you turned me down. And why do you have to make that comment to me? Is it possible for you to make the first move for a change? Yes, we probably do a problem and it's you! I'm sick of the way you to talk to me sometimes. I've had enough of it and enough of you.'

I filled with tears. 'Well, I've had enough too,' I said.

'Well, we both agree on something,' he shouted.

I put the magazine down and went upstairs and locked myself in the bathroom. I sat on the toilet seat and cried my eyes out. I had all sorts of things going through my mind as I snivelled.

'Is this the end of us?' 'Why does he have to be so nasty?' 'Has Sebastian met somebody else?'

Sebastian would normally come after me if we had a row, but this time, he didn't. This made me worse, thinking that he didn't care anymore.

I sat upstairs in the bathroom for about a half hour crying. I had heart palpitations, and my hands were shaking. My life was in ruins. To top it all, I still had really bad tummy pains, and the argument made it worse. The tissue I was using was all scrunched up and wet. I had cried that much.

I eventually stopped crying and washed my face. I went back into the bedroom and sat on the end of the bed looking in the mirror. What has happened to me? I thought. I looked a right mess, my hair looked limp, my face was all red, and I looked like a fat blubber.

I didn't go back downstairs that day. I thought it best not to. I got changed into some comfy pj's and got in bed. I spent the rest of the day on the iPad and reading a book. I couldn't face going downstairs for another argument. I was surprised Sebastian didn't come up to me, maybe he felt it best left for the day.

I fell asleep in bed around 9.00 pm; Sebastian was still downstairs.

I woke up about 6.00 am. It was nice and sunny outside. I looked to the side and noticed that Sebastian wasn't there. His side of the bed was very tidy, so he obviously hadn't been to bed. Well, not in this bed. I got up and sneaked downstairs to see if he was on the sofa, but he wasn't. There were beer cans on the table, so he must have had a few drinks the night before. I looked out the window and noticed his car still there; that was a relief.

I sat quietly on the sofa drinking tea until about 9.00 am when I heard some movement upstairs. Sebastian had slept in the spare room. We had never slept apart from the day we got married, and the thought it had come to this made me cry again.

'How on earth had we got to this?' I thought.

Sebastian came downstairs and went straight into the kitchen and made himself a drink. He didn't say anything at all to me. I went into the kitchen after ten minutes. Sebastian was sitting at the table with his cup of tea playing on his phone; he didn't even look up at me to acknowledge me.

My heart palpitations started again as I said. 'You slept in the spare bed.'

'Yep,' he replied, still not looking at me.

'Sebastian, I don't want us to be like this. I'm so sorry.'

'Nope, I don't want this either,' he replied.

My heart sank as I asked, 'Where do we go from here?'

'Not sure, Charlie. We can't carry on like this, I do know that. You're not the same person lately.'

'What do you mean?'

'You were always happy and loving. Lately, you have been so moody. I can't talk to you; you have no patience, and you shout and moan about the smallest of things. I told you the other week, it's like treading on eggshells; it's no fun for me.'

I felt tears strolling down my face, the emotions filled the whole of my body.

'We've never slept apart since we've been married,' I cried.

'I needed some space, Charlie.'

I went over to him and put my arms around his neck.

I cried, 'I love you so much. I don't know what's wrong with me. I'll try harder. I promise, let's not give up now.'

Sebastian was very cold with me. He reluctantly put one arm around me.

'Let's see, Charlie, something has to change.'

'I promise, I'll change,' I cried.

'Go sort yourself out,' Sebastian said, 'you need to wash your face and clean yourself up.'

I let go of him and went upstairs to have a shower. I felt more alone and mixed up than ever. I didn't eat at all that day. I felt so sick with anguish and fear of being on my own, not being loved by Sebastian anymore.

That weekend was the worst ever. I thought it was all over for us. I knew I needed to control my emotions and try and be a better person. Depression was taking over, and I needed to change my mood. I had never seen Sebastian like this before; if it hadn't been a lockdown, I think he would have left.

That Sunday got even better. I came on my period on Sunday night, a couple of days earlier if you went by the period day's and dismissed the intermittent bleeding. I chose not to say anything to Sebastian. I wished for everything to get back to some normality. I took some painkillers to ease my tummy pains before going to bed.

Sebastian got in the same bed as me on that Sunday; at least that was a start, I thought.

The following few weeks were much of a muchness. Sebastian was still very cold with me, albeit a little better than the weekend we had the big argument. He kept out of my way most of the time, still training and running. I continued to have good and bad days, tearful days, and days full of anxiety.

Shopping was a pain in the backside, having to queue to get in the supermarket and limited to amounts you could buy. I hated the weekly ritual; it took twice as long to do the shopping.

I often wondered if we weren't in lockdown, would Sebastian and I still be together?

The best day in April was Summer's birthday, April 16th, she was twenty-one. Originally, we had planned to have a family party at home with friends. She didn't want a big party, so I was going to put a small buffet on for her at the house. All of this was cancelled due to lockdown. I had also planned for us to have a spa day and meal together the following Saturday, but we were unable to do it that too. Luckily, I had already got her birthday card before lockdown, which I had posted to her. Sebastian and I agreed to transfer some money to Summer for her birthday as we couldn't do all the things we had planned. I secretly had things delivered to her, one item being a white sweatshirt with Legend since 1999 written on it, another being an apron with Legend since 1999 on it; they were only small things, but things she could keep for remembering her twenty-first.

In the evening, we had a Zoom party. There was Sebastian and I, Summer and Chris, and Mitch on the Zoom. We watched Summer open her presents and sang happy birthday to her. We had prosecco and beers whilst on the call to make it more like a party. She was overjoyed with all her money and presents. We agreed that we would do a spa and meal in a few months once out of lockdown. I could not believe it had been twenty-one years since Summer had been born; it felt like yesterday. Sebastian and I were civilised on the call. We didn't want to let Summer know we were going through a rough time. Sebastian did put his arm around me on the Zoom, probably all for show for the kids.

CHAPTER 15
FIRST HALF OF MAY 2020

May approached very fast. Nothing much had changed between Sebastian and I; we hadn't had sex for a few months, and I was convinced we would split after lockdown. The weather started off good in May. The sun was out most days, and the temperature was above twenty degrees. This made life a lot easier; we spent time out in the garden sunbathing. The sun gave us a good life feeling.

The Early May Bank Holiday moved to a Friday this year; the weather was glorious, Sebastian and I sat out in the garden. We had shopped for plenty of beer and prosecco knowing the weather was forecast good. We sat outside and started drinking very early, by lunch time we were both tipsy. I had put my bikini on as it was so hot. I took a chance; I was due on my period on the Sunday or maybe before with all the intermittent bleeding I'd had, I had lost track; it became the norm for me. In fact, I felt the norm in general had changed, Sebastian and I had changed, everything was different.

Sebastian was drinking quite fast, and he kept topping my glass up every time he got a fresh beer.

'C'mon, my dear, you're slowing up,' he kept saying.

He hadn't been that nice to me in a few weeks, since we'd had the argument.

By about 2.00 pm, we were both very drunk. I went inside to get us another drink, and Sebastian followed me in. As I walked out of the kitchen into the lounge with our fresh drinks, he grabbed me and started kissing me on the neck. This was the first time in ages he had made a move on me. He took the drinks out of my hand and put them on the table, then started to kiss my neck again. He looked at me in the eyes.

'I love you, Charlie,' he said as he grabbed my face and kissed me on the lips.

We started snogging like young teenagers, and for the first time in a few months I felt wanted. Sebastian undid my bikini and slowly pulled the straps down my arms, so it fell onto the floor.

'I want you so much,' he said as he moved from kissing me on the lips, to the neck and gradually down to my breasts. He sucked on my nipples so hard. We hadn't been like this for such a long time, and it felt so good.

Sebastian pushed me on the arm of the sofa so that I was leaning on it. He still sucked on each nipple hard as he moved his hand between my legs. He started to feel in between my legs moving his hand up and down to arouse me. I could feel myself getting wet.

'That's so good,' I said.

Very slowly, Sebastian moved my bikini bottoms to the side and started to touch me.

'You're so wet,' he said.

His legs were between my legs, he started to gradually open his legs to push my legs apart even more. He slowly started to push one finger inside me; it felt so good. I put my head forward on his shoulder and started to moan.

'Are you okay,' he whispered as he started to move from kissing my breasts back up to my neck.

I leant back and replied, 'Yes, couldn't be better.'

He kissed me on the lips and gradually slipped a second finger inside me. He gradually moved his fingers back and forth inside me. I felt so tuned on. I put my hand between his legs and could feel his penis so hard.

'You're gonna make me come,' I cried.

On that, he pulled my bikini bottoms down and knelt. He started kissing me on the top of the legs, then he pulled my legs apart and started kissing my virginal area. He started licking me so gently, then his tongue pushed hard against my clitorises, swirling round and round.

I was so turned on and screamed, 'Oh god, I'm coming.'

Sebastian continued to lick me so vigorously. I was so aroused. My heart began to beat quicker, and I started to breath faster. My breasts nipples became erect, and my muscles started to tighten all over my body.

Sebastian got off his knees and pulled off his shorts and boxers whilst kissing me on the lips. He pushed his penis inside me. It slipped in easily, I was so wet. He slowly pushed his penis back and forth, whilst pushing deeper each time. He pushed me back more on the sofa and grabbed my legs up to wrap them around his shoulders. He held me in position with his arms wrapped around me whilst kissing me hard on the lips.

'I'm coming, Charlie,' he shouted.

'Ooh ooh,' he said as he pushed deeper inside me.

Sebastian pushed hard for a couple of more times, then everything went still; he leant his head on my shoulder. Shortly after, his penis started to soften, and he kissed me on the head. I released my legs from around his shoulders. He gently released his penis from my Virginia and held it while he walked off to the toilet. I went off upstairs to clean up.

When I got back downstairs, Sebastian was pulling his shorts back on. He held my hand and said, 'That was lovely, Charlie. I love you loads. Let's enjoy the last bit of the sun and have a nice romantic meal tonight.'

I smiled at him as he led me back into the garden, holding my hand.

This was the breakthrough we needed. I honestly thought we were at the end. It felt so nice to be held again and to be loved. For the first time in a while, I felt a glint of hope that things were going to be okay. We both still felt a bit tipsy, but we managed to get in the kitchen and cook a lovely meal. Sebastian cooked my favourite cheese and potato pie, and I cooked bread and butter pudding for dessert, Sebastian's favourite.

We sat at the table in the conservatory for the meal and continued to drink more alcohol. We put some romantic music on in the background and reminisced about the past. We didn't bother with the TV; it was too depressing with all the news on the pandemic. Sebastian reached across and held my hand.

'We'll be okay, Charlie, just talk to me.'

I kissed him on the hand and smiled.

On that note, Sebastian's mobile started to ring.

'Oh, its Summer,' he said.

He got up from the table and started to walk around whilst answering his mobile. I cleared the table while he was talking to Summer, I heard him say, 'Yea, your mom and I are having a bit of a date night.'

I smiled at him, and he winked back as I cleared the last of the dishes.

That night in bed, Sebastian put his arms around me and held me tight. It felt so nice. I felt loved again, and we fell asleep snuggled up to each other.

I woke up late on Saturday morning; it was 8.30 am. I looked over at Sebastian to see he was still fast asleep or so I thought. As I got out of bed, he piped up, 'You're not getting up, are you?'

'It's half past eight; it's really late,' I replied.

'What's there to do, Charlie? We're in lockdown. Go get us a nice cup of tea and bring it back to bed.' He smiled

I smiled and went downstairs and made us a drink. I got back in bed with my drink and sipped it slowly. I couldn't help but think, was it the drink the day before and were we going to be back to where we were in a miserable relationship. Sebastian drank his tea. He then leaned over and pulled me to towards him, putting his arm around me. I rested my head on his chest, and he rubbed his hand up and down my back.

After a few minutes, he pulled my head up from his chest with his hand and started to kiss me. We kissed and snogged for a good couple of minutes. Slowly, Sebastian moved his hands on my legs and pulled up my nightshirt, lifting me up to pull it over my head. We both lay on our sides naked kissing each other. He rubbed his hands through my hair and kissed me intimately.

I moved my hand to his penis and started to move it slowly backwards and forwards. His penis was getting harder and harder.

'That's nice, babe,' he said.

Sebastian pushed my legs open with his hand and started to touch me. He slowly entered one finger inside me. I knew he was really turned on, he started talking dirty.

'Get on top, babe, and fuck me.'

He pulled myself gently on top of him and he pushed my legs apart with his legs. I sat up on top of him and slowly moved his penis up and down my vagina lubricating myself. Slowly, his penis entered my vagina. I pushed myself down on him so that it went deeper inside. Sebastian held me at the bottom of the back and slowly moved in motion with me up and down. This went on for about five minutes, then we started to move faster and breathed much heavier. Sebastian moved his hands to my breasts, one in each hand, caressing them as his penis moved in and out. I leant forward to put my breasts close to his face, so that Sebastian could kiss and bite my nipples; we were both so turned on.

Sebastian then pushed me off and pulled me off the bed. He asked me to turn around and bend over the bed; it was nice to be domineered. He pushed me down on the bed front ways and opened my legs. Sebastian was still very strong, fit, and muscular. It felt good for him to take control. He held his penis in his hand and moved it slowly across my vaginal area, and gently, he pushed it inside me and lay on top of me. I can't remember the last we had had sex from behind; it had been a number of years.

Sebastian lay on top of me, slowly moving backwards and forwards. I felt his penis inside me more so in this position; it felt very deep. He put his arms around me and held one breast in each hand, feeling my nipples. He kissed the back of neck.

'I love being inside you, Charlie,' he whispered in my ear as he breathed heavily.

'Tell me when you're going to come,' he said.

'Ooh, it's so good,' I said. 'I want you to fuck me hard, make me come.'

Sebastian pushed his penis harder inside me. I grabbed his hand from my right breast and put it up to my mouth. I put his finger in my mouth and started to suck on it as if I were sucking his penis. We were both sweating; it was a hot morning with the sun shining in adding to the sexual heat from the activity in the room. Sebastian moved his other hand from my left breast down to my vagina and started touching me up around where his penis was, causing my clitorises to be even more wet.

'God, I'm coming,' I shouted.

'Are you coming, babe? Tell me your coming,' Sebastian shouted.

We screamed out, moaned, and climaxed together. Sebastian lay on top of me for a while before lifting himself off me to take a shower.

I lay frontwards on the bed for about ten minutes whilst Sebastian took a shower. Maybe I was wrong and yesterday was not a drunken moment; it definitely felt good compared to of late.

The rest of day was good. We went for a long walk, held hands, and talked about the kids, and what we were going to do for the rest of the weekend. We agreed to have a BBQ on that afternoon and make the best of the weather.

Things seemed to be much better, and I could see a light at the end of the tunnel.

On the afternoon, we got the BBQ out and cooked chicken, steaks, burgers, and ribs. We had several alcoholic drinks too; it was still very hot. Sebastian had his top off and shorts on, I had to keep spraying him with suntan oil. I put a bikini on again as it was so hot. Sebastian did all the cooking; he loved a meat feast and was particular how he liked the meat cooked. He would have the steak rare. I preferred it well done. The thought of blood coming out if it made me feel sick. We had so much fun.

I went inside to get some mayonnaise out of the kitchen. As I turned around to walk back in, Sebastian was behind me.

'Come here you,' he said.

He pulled at my hair and started snogging me hard.

'I want you now, right here,' he said.

I was a little sore from the morning, but I didn't want to disappoint Sebastian, so I decided to give him a blow job to satisfy him. I pulled his shorts down whilst we were kissing and snogging. Sebastian leant up against the kitchen unit whilst I leant down on the floor. I hadn't seen his penis full on like this in my face for a while. I slowly moved his penis back and forth in my hand as it got harder and harder. With my other hand, I felt and rubbed his balls.

'These are full, babe, they need emptying,' I said.

'That's good, Charlie, don't stop,' he panted.

I put my face to his penis and started to kiss his balls whilst also feeling them with my one hand. I slowly moved my mouth to kiss and caress his penis. I put his penis in my mouth and slowly sucked on it, moving it back and forth.

Sebastian held my head with his hands and moved it back and forth. I stopped for a second and grabbed the mayonnaise off the side. I squirted some in my hand and rubbed it over Sebastian's penis. I then licked it off nice and slowly. Sebastian loved this; it wasn't something we'd ever done before.

'Tastes good, babe,' I said as I slowly moved my tongue back to the end of his penis.

I sucked slowly to start and then as Sebastian started to moan, I sucked harder and faster.

'I want you to come over me,' I said.

Whilst I was still sucking Sebastian, he'd undone my bikini top and started to feel my breasts.

'Babe, I'm coming. I'm coming, oh ooh,' he said as he pulled his penis out of my mouth and came all over my breasts.

We laughed. 'I'll get you some tissues,' I said as I walked off to the bathroom.

We enjoyed the rest of the day with laughter. In the evening, we did a Zoom party with Summer and Mitch. It was the best Saturday I'd had in a long time.

We had so much fun on the Zoom; it was lovely to see the kids, they are our life. They commented how happy we both looked. I must admit, I didn't feel that about them, they both looked stressed out.

The evening was very warm, and Sebastian suggested for me to sleep with nothing on like he did to keep cool. I was so hot, so I did strip off in the night to cool down.

Sunday morning, we both woke lying in bed completely naked. I had bad stomach cramps again.

'You look beautiful naked, Charlie.'

I pulled the quilt over me and said, 'I wish I felt that way.'

Sebastian leant over and kissed me. 'You're not twenty-one anymore. Stop putting yourself down; you have a wonderful body.'

We started kissing, and Sebastian pulled his body on top of mine. He breathed heavily as he slowly moved down to kiss my breasts and suck my nipples.

Three days in a row I thought, can't be bad!!

Sebastian had good bicep muscles, he held himself up as if he were doing a press up and gradually pushed his penis into me; it was very slow and intimate. He kissed me slowly and held my hands above my head so I couldn't interfere with his sexual fantasy. He moved faster as he climaxed. This time it was more intimate, no foreplay with each other, but very romantic and slow. We had the chance to tell each other how much we loved each other and enjoyed making love together. After we finished, Sebastian held me tight in his arms for a while, kissing me on the head, rubbing my arms, and gripping onto my hands. Our marriage and come alive again; the love was always there.

I was the first to get up. I went to the toilet and noticed blood on the tissue. It looked as if I had started my period. Sebastian went to the family bathroom to clean himself up. I went back to the bedroom

'Did you have a bit of blood?'

Sebastian said. 'Yes I did, but don't worry; it's okay.'

I replied, 'Not sure if it's my period or what. I've been bleeding a lot of as late.'

Sebastian held my hand and pulled me on the side of the bed next to him.

'Charlie, this is my point when I said about menopause some time back. It can affect everyone differently. You should get it checked, Charlie, to be on the safe side.'

I nodded, 'Yes, I will.'

Well, the first half of May had gone well for us in lockdown. I felt closer than ever to Sebastian.

CHAPTER 16
SECOND HALF OF MAY 2020

I started my period on Sunday 10th May, as normal. I felt tired and had anxiety. I'd tried my hardest not to argue after the big row in April, and it appeared we were getting on much better. Sebastian was so good this month. He knew it was my monthly period, and he was very sympathetic. He rubbed my tummy at times and made all my meals; he said he knew all the ingredients to help women during their menstrual cycle. I just went along with it; I wasn't actually sure anybody knew how I felt or knew what foods to eat.

Sebastian and I were more aligned this month. We went out for walks once daily together, spending more time looking at nature. It was lovely to see the birds, the green leaves on the trees, and smell the freshness from the farmland when we walked across the field. At one point, I suggested to Sebastian that we should have a picnic one day on the field, like teenage kids for a laugh. Sebastian squeezed my hand tight for a second, which meant he agreed with me.

We had a holiday booked early June to go to Turkey with TUI. We received confirmation that day that it was cancelled. No surprises, that was what we expected, nobody was travelling anywhere at the moment. Tui offered us vouchers plus a twenty percent discount voucher. Sebastian and I agreed to hold on to the vouchers until the end of the year before asking for a refund. We decided to wait and see what was happening in the travel world.

About two days into my period, I woke with a sudden need to have a wee. I jumped out of bed and got to the toilet just in time. It really stung and burnt as I wee'd and not much came out. The burning sensation hurt so much, and as I got off the toilet, I felt the need to pee again. This continued for about a half hour. I didn't move out of the bathroom.

Sebastian wondered where I was.

'Are you okay, Charlie? You've been in the bathroom ages,' he shouted.

'Yes, I'm fine, coming now.'

I flushed the toilet and washed my hands. Just on that, I felt the need to wee again. I sat back on the toilet and dribbled little bits; I couldn't wee properly although my bladder felt full.

'What is wrong now?' I thought.

I eventually went back in the bedroom and got in bed.

'I thought you'd fell down the toilet, babe; you've been in their ages.' Sebastian laughed.

'It's hurting me to wee and stinging like mad.'

'Oh, that's not right. I wonder what's causing that?' he asked.

'Don't know. I'll have to get something from the chemist, though. I can't have this all day.'

I got up and walked to our local chemist. Good it was only a five-minute walk, I was absolutely dying for another pee. It was weird at the chemist; they only allowed two people in at a time, and it was a one-way system. They also had Perspex screens up to shelter the pharmacist. I explained the problem to them, and they said it was probably cystitis. They gave me some sachets to take, and said if it was no better in a few days to contact my GP for some antibiotics. I couldn't wait to get home to have another pee!

I took the sachets throughout the day; it helped massively. By the end of the day, I felt much better. I continued to finish off the course. I googled cystitis to see what it was. I was amazed to read that it could be an infection as a result of sexual intercourse. I laughed to myself, well we'd certainly enjoyed sex for a few days, maybe that was the cause of it.

By Saturday 16th May, I had finished my period and the cystitis had completely cleared up. Sebastian had gone over the neighbours to do a gym work out, so I did a body pump work out. When I'd finished, I had a shower and decided to surprise Sebastian. I made up my face with some makeup, put on some sexy black lacey underwear with some fishnet stockings and watched out the window for him to come back. I remembered when we were younger and how he loved me to dress in sexy underwear and stockings. I hadn't done this for ages. After about five minutes, I saw Sebastian walking back to the house.

He came in the house and went into the kitchen and made himself a protein shake; he normally did this after he had worked out.

He shouted, 'Where are you, Charlie?'

'I'm just upstairs. I'm coming down now,' I shouted back.

I put a trench coat on the top of my underwear and some high heal shoes. I had butterflies in my stomach; the thought that we were going to have sex again. I hadn't dressed up for a long time or even put make up on since the lockdown.

I walked downstairs carefully, the shoes were very high, and the last thing I wanted was to fall down the stairs and make a tit of myself. As I got to the bottom stair, I saw Sebastian sitting on the coach in the lounge, opening his mail. He didn't look up; he was too busy with the mail. I walked over to the lounge door.

'Anything you fancy?' I asked

He looked up at me. 'Wow, look at you,' he replied.

I walked over to him and stood in front of him. I slowly undid the belt on my trench coat and opened the coat, letting it slip off me gradually on to the floor.

I could see the excitement in Sebastian's face.

I slowly moved towards him and sat on top of him on the couch.

'You look so sexy,' Sebastian said as he pulled me close to him and kissed me.

I loved the sitting position with myself on top. I felt in control. It had been a while since we had sex in this position. Sebastian was really turned on by my underwear and stockings. He moved his hands up and down my legs, feeling my stockings, then he pulled on the back my thong. This reminded me so much of the time at Sebastian's mom's, when she heard us having sex downstairs on the sofa after a drunken night out.

He slowly moved up to feeling both breasts, one in each hand. He kissed my neck as he moved one hand behind to undo my bra. He seemed to be struggling to undo it.

I laughed. 'Are you struggling, my dear? Never struggled before.'

He laughed and managed to undo the hook. My bra straps fell down my arms, and Sebastian pulled it off and flung it on the floor. He started to kiss my neck and moved slowly down to me breasts. He started to bite on my nipples, taking each breast in turn.

'I love your tits,' he said.

I wasn't exactly small. I was a 38D, much bigger than when I was younger, the joys of getting older. Sebastian seemed not to complain about that, though; the bigger the better; he loved big boobs.

I moved from his lap on to my knees on the floor and pulled his shorts and boxers down. Sebastian lifted his body up to make it easier. He had a hard on, and I kissed his penis while he put his head back on the sofa.

'That's lovely, babe, don't stop,' he said.

I put his penis in my mouth, and I sucked very slowly. I wanted this to be a long intimate session. Sebastian looked down at me and watched as I sucked his penis. I then held one breast either side of his penis and began to move them to masturbate his penis. This really turned him on; he held one breast in each hand to assist me and to move and push my breasts harder against his penis.

After a couple of minutes, he said, 'Get on top of me, babe.'

I lifted myself up whilst at the same time removing my thong. I pulled myself up on to the sofa back into a sitting position on top of Sebastian.

'Do you want it?' I asked.

He kissed me hard on the lips. 'I want to be inside you.'

I moved my hand down and held his penis, gradually moving it across my vagina to make myself wet. As I got wet, I pushed myself down on to his penis, slowly guiding it inside me. Once his penis was inside me, I pushed down hard.

'That's so good, babe, can you feel it?'

I moaned, 'It's so deep, babe.'

Sebastian put one hand on either side of my bum and helped me manoeuvre slowly up and down. We kissed each other intimately and breathed heavily together enjoying the moment. After a few minutes, we began to move faster.

'Make me come, Charlie.'

I pushed harder and faster. My breasts were bouncing about. I pushed them closer to Sebastian's face so that he could suck and bite on them.

'I'm coming, babe, I'm coming,' Sebastian shouted.

I pushed harder than ever on his penis. He went stiff and all his muscles clamped up. I knew he was climaxing. He put his head back on the sofa with his eyes closed whilst still holding me tight on top of him.

There was silence for a while; I knew he had come. He then opened his eyes and looked at me.

'You certainly know how to turn me on, Charlie.'

I smiled and kissed him. 'It's a woman's prerogative to keep her man satisfied.'

He laughed and tapped me on the bum. I knew this was a nod for me to get off him. I slowly got up off Sebastian, letting his penis release slowly out of me. As I did so, some sperm run down my legs and onto Sebastian.

'I'll get some tissue; wait there,' I said.

I went to the bathroom and wiped myself and my leg, grabbed some tissue, and took it to Sebastian.

'Thanks,' he said as he wiped his penis; it was still erect as he wiped it.

'I love you in high heels and stockings,' he said as he got up, tapped my bum, and went to the bathroom.

I knew Sebastian loved me dressing up. I hadn't done it for a long time.

We enjoyed the rest of the day out in the garden. We needed to go food shopping, but the weather was too nice to spend in queues; instead, we sat on our loungers and had a few beers.

Saturday night we had another Zoom party with Summer and Mitch; this had become a weekly ritual. Every day was the same to us, but for Summer and Mitch it was still the weekend, and they were still working hard.

'Mom, you look so tanned; you look like you've been away,' Summer said.

'We've only been in the garden,' I replied. 'It's been very hot, so I've had my bikini on.'

'You don't look as tanned as Mom, Dad,' Summer said.

'Your mom tans easily, Summer, she's a sun worshipper.' He laughed.

Mitch asked, 'What you both been up to?'

Sebastian jumped in. 'Errm, not a lot, just in the garden.'

If only they knew what we were getting up to. We hadn't had sex like this before, not for a very long time; in fact, it was even better than when we were younger.

The kids talked about their experiences at work. I felt a little guilty when I heard what they were both going through. Poor Summer was working on a Covid ward with patients. They still hadn't got the right PE to do their job safely. This annoyed us; surely, they should be protected if they were expected to work on these wards. Sebastian went mad, this was the first time I'd saw anger in his face since the time we had the big argument in April. Mitch was also working hard in the bank coordinating the loan facilities to help support businesses. We were very proud of what they were doing. We all had a drink in our hand to say cheers, we missed and loved them so much.

I had adjusted to the lockdown and was enjoying life with Sebastian; we hadn't spent time alone together like this since we were young. I thought it was going to be disastrous in the beginning, but it has turned out okay.

After the Zoom call, Sebastian went on about Summer and that she should refuse to go to work if they haven't got the right equipment. Summer was still his blue-eyed baby; she knew that she could twist him round her little finger.

'If anything happens to Summer, I tell you, they won't like me,' he said.

'Who won't like you?'

'The bloody government and the hospital,' he replied.

I did agree with him, but I thought it best to keep quiet.

The rest of May continued the same; we had weekly Zoom meetings with the kids to make sure they were okay, and we both worked out three times a week and drank more and more alcohol. Th sex continued; we tried so many different positions, doggy style, sitting style, 69 and reverse style. The sex got better and better each week, the best it had ever been.

At the end of May, Boris Johnson announced some relaxing to the lockdown.

In England, Mr Johnson said groups of up to six people can meet in private gardens "provided those from different households continue to stick to social distancing rules" by staying two metres apart.

The rules will come into force on Monday, June 1.

Sebastian and I were so excited; at last, we could see the kids. We had missed them so much.

CHAPTER 17

JUNE 2020

Friday the 29th of May 2020 was another great day for sex. The weather was good, and Sebastian and I sat outside on sun loungers drinking prosecco. I wore a floral knee length dress with nothing underneath; it was too warm. As usual, Sebastian wore some swim shorts with no top. He looked sexy with his strong big biceps bulging out. Sebastian was still tall, dark, and very handsome.

It was about lunchtime, he called over to me.

'Another drink, Charlie?'

I was reading a book. 'Hmm, yes, thank you, hun'.

Sebastian got me another prosecco, and as he passed me the glass, he stood in front of me. He had his dark sunglasses on and took a sip from his drink. I couldn't quite work out where he was looking. I smiled to myself and bought my knees up on the sun lounger so as to put my two feet adjacent to each other. My dress lifted slightly so that Sebastian could see everything down below.

He looked and smiled. 'You are one hell of a dirty bitch, Charlie. Are you doing a Sharon Stone on me?'

I laughed. 'As if.'

He leant over to me and kissed me on the lips.

'I think you need seeing to,' he whispered as he grabbed my hand and pulled me up out of the chair. He took the glass out of my hand and put it on the table.

He kept hold of my hand and pulled me behind him upstairs. As soon as we got in the bedroom, he stripped off and lay on the bed. His penis lay semi hard to the right side. Whenever I saw him in his boxers or jeans, I could tell his penis always lays to the right side.

'Strip off,' he asked.

'What?' I asked.

'I want you to strip naked for me.'

I have never had the confidence to do this before, but I stood at the end of the bed while he watched me. I slowly lowered the straps on my dress and let it fall from me to the floor. I was standing at the end of bed completely naked.

'Touch yourself,' Sebastian said.

I felt a little uncomfortable but moved my hand down to my vagina and slowly moved my fingers around to arouse myself.

He sat up slightly and said, 'Come here to me.'

I stopped touching myself and crawled on the bed up to him. He kissed me slowly and gently and rubbed his hands into my back firmly. He pushed me down on my back whilst still kissing me.

'Close your eyes,' he whispered.

I closed my eyes for a short time, then kept peeping to see what he was doing.

'Charlie, close them tight.'

I started to laugh. 'I'm trying.'

Sebastian reached over to my bedside cabinet and pulled out a blackout eye mask I had.

He pulled the mask over my head saying, 'Put this on.'

Now I was in total darkness and didn't know what was going to happen next. He licked my lips and put his tongue in my mouth. It was very sexy not being able to see what was going to happen next. The next thing I heard was a kind of vibration noise. What has he got and what was he going to do? I thought.

Sebastian rubbed an instrument against my vaginal area. 'Relax, Charlie, and trust me.'

It didn't take long for me to work out it was a vibrator. We had never ever used sex toys or instruments before; this was a first. Sebastian used his thumb and forefinger of his right hand to pull the lips aside on my vagina whilst rubbing the vibrator against my clit in circles.

I couldn't see a thing and felt completely out of control, but the sensation was turning me on. The wetter I got, the farther Sebastian pushed the vibrator to enter inside me. I had never felt this sensation before. My muscles started to tighten, and I felt turned on more than ever; I started to scream

'Relax, babe, and enjoy it.'

'Sebastian, I'm so wet; I'm going to come. Oh god, not yet.'

He pulled the vibrator out and pushed his penis inside me. I was so wet that it slid in without much pushing too hard.

'I'm going to come with you, babe,' he said.

I still couldn't see what was going on. Sebastian thrusted himself into me so hard and fast. I wrapped my legs around his body whilst he kissed and caressed my breasts, biting hard on my nipples.

'Are you coming, babe' he whispered in my ear.

'Oh, I'm coming, babe; don't stop,' I shouted.

Sebastian slapped me at the side of my leg 'C'mon, babe, let's ride and come together.'

I hadn't had the slapping before, so this was a total surprise to me, so was the blind folding to be honest.

I felt my muscles tighten, and my whole body started to stiffen and shake.

We both came together; I still couldn't see anything. Sebastian lay still for a while on top of me. He then pulled the blindfold off and kissed me on the forehead.

He looked at me., 'I love you so much, Charlie.'

I looked deep into his eyes and kissed him on the cheek. 'I love you too, Sebastian.'

He put his forehead against mine for a short time, then lifted himself up off me and went to the bathroom. I sat up and noticed blood on the sheet. 'Oh, shit, I thought.'

I got up off the bed to take a further look. There was a circle of blood on the sheet. I knew it was from me; how embarrassing was this. Sebastian walked back out of the bathroom; he could see I was destressed over something

'What's up, babe?' he asked.

I felt so embarrassed and started to cry. 'I think I've started to bleed again. I'm so sorry. I didn't know, I mean I'm not due on my period; it just happened again.'

Sebastian walked over to me and looked at the bed. 'Hey, come here.'

He put his arms around me and held me tight, kissing me on the head. He wiped the tears away from my face.

'It's fine, Charlie, we'll clean it up; it's no big deal.'

I sniffed. 'Maybe it was the vibrator.'

Sebastian sat on the edge of the bed and pulled me to him.

'Charlie, I mentioned the menopause to you last month; it maybe that. I'm no expert on the subject, but you need to get things checked at the doctors. This has gone on a few months, and it needs checking. I love you so much and want to make sure you are okay.'

He went on, 'Promise me you will call the doctor.'

I wiped another tear away. 'Yes, I will.'

'That's my girl,' he replied.

He pinched my chin. 'Let's get the bed cleaned up and changed.'

We got on with stripping the bed down.

'Where did you get that vibrator from?' I asked.

Sebastian smiled. 'It was a present from your mates for your fortieth birthday for a joke.'

'Oh my god; I remember that. It was years ago.'

He laughed. 'Yes I know. We put it up in the wardrobe away from the kids. I found it out the other week and thought we could have some fun with it now we're alone.'

I laughed. 'I'd forgot it was there.'

'You enjoyed it, though?' he asked.

'Yes, it was different; not something we've done before.'

'If we ever do anything you don't want to do, Charlie, or you feel uncomfortable, tell me.'

'No, I'm okay, Sebastian.'

We carried on and stripped the bed down. For the first time in a long time, we spoke about sex, and I felt comfortable talking to him. Last month, I would never have spoken to Sebastian about sex or my problems.

I continued bleeding all weekend and felt totally drained. I had a bit of a wobble on the Sunday. I didn't sleep well on the Saturday night and had hot sweats. I was overtired Sunday, making me irritable. Sebastian and I decided to go shopping; it was horrific, there was long queues, and they were out of stock of a lot of things.

'There's nothing here. What's the point in the store opening?' I snapped.

Sebastian never commented.

I called an assistant over. 'Excuse me, do you have any cider vinegar?' She replied, 'It's down the second isle.'

I walked off to go down the aisle and she shouted back, 'Excuse me, madam, you can't go that way; it's one way, you need to follow the signs.'

'I only want to get the cider vinegar from that isle,' I replied.

'Sorry, madam, you need to go this way.'

I could feel myself boiling up. 'Everyone else appeared to be doing what they like, why were we different? The vinegar was only there, a few metres away.'

'Madam, can you please follow the arrows,' she repeated.

'I tell you what. I'll never shop here again; there's nothing on the shelves,' I shouted.

Sebastian walked off embarrassed. The assistant also walked off and chose to ignore me. I was more irritable than ever, and everything was a problem, my whole body and muscles were aching. The lack of sleep was also catching up with me.

I walked fast to catch up with Sebastian.

'Do you have to cause a scene?' he asked.

'Well, all I wanted was something from the aisle close to me and she was telling to walk all the way round when nobody else was.'

'Why are we different?' I asked

'Charlie, just stop going on and let's get out of here. They are only trying to do their job.'

I knew he wasn't happy with me. Sebastian never like confrontation.

Sebastian hardly spoke the rest of the day. We put the shopping away when we got home and said very little to each other.

Monday was the start of a new month, June, we continued into lockdown. Sebastian and I got up early and went for a walk together. He held my hand but didn't say much. When we got home, he said, 'I'm going for a workout if that's okay?'

'Yea, sure.'

He pulled on my arm. 'Please ring the doctor, babe.'

I smiled. 'I will, I promise.'

Whilst Sebastian was out training, I looked up menopause symptoms on the internet. It read:

+ Hot flushes
+ Night sweats
+ Vaginal dryness and discomfort during sex
+ Difficulty sleeping
+ Low mood or anxiety
+ Reduced sex drive (libido)
+ Problems with memory and concentration
+ Irregular periods

I had certainly been suffering from a lot of these problems, except for reduced sex drive as late. I knew in my own mind it was time to call the doctor. What if the bleeding was something more serious? I had put it off long enough, and Sebastian was right. I needed to get it checked to make sure I was okay.

I called the doctor's surgery and got through to the reception.

'I'd like to make an appointment to see the doctor.'

'Can I take your name and date of birth?' the receptionist asked.

I gave my details to the receptionist.

'Can you confirm your address, please?' she asked.

I relayed our home address.

'Okay, thank you, Charlotte, the doctor is only seeing emergencies in the surgery due to Covid-19. Can you explain to me what is wrong, and we will review your case,' she said.

I started to fill with tears. I didn't know why, maybe it was making that initial call. My emotions suddenly got carried away with me. This was the first time I was going to talk about the menopause.

'Well, I have been bleeding between my periods for about three months now, and it's starting to get me down. I've had times when I burst into tears for no reason, and I find I have no patience with anything.'

I paused for a while; tears ran down my face as I continued, 'Sometimes, I feel like I could smash the room up. I've ignored the bleeding, but I've eventually plugged the courage up to call you.'

'That's the best thing, Charlotte, calling us. You've made a big step forward; this does need checking. I've noted down everything what you've said, and the doctor will give you a call back for a consultation in the next few hours.'

The receptionist confirmed my mobile number. For the first time, I wiped my eyes and felt a sigh of relief that I had finally spoken to somebody.

It was only about a half hour, when my mobile rang. I picked it up to see it was the doctor.

'Hello, Charlotte, it's Doctor James here.'

'Hi, Doctor, thank you for calling,' I replied.

'I have some notes here, Charlotte, but can you tell me more about what's been happening?' Doctor James asked.

'Well, I've been bleeding between my periods now for about three months. I know we're in lockdown, but I get so anxious and cry over the silliest of things. I could have killed my husband a few months ago. I get so angry over things and have very little impatience. I don't sleep very well; I often wake up in the night all hot and bothered.'

Doctor James laughed. 'It very much sounds like your perimenopausal, Charlotte, but we need to get it checked. Are your smears up to date?'

'Yes, I only had one about twelve months ago,' I replied.

'Okay, that's good.'

'What's the difference between perimenopausal and menopause?' I asked inquisitively.

'Well, Charlotte, perimenopause is the first stage of this process and can start eight to ten years before menopause. Menopause is the point when a woman no longer has menstrual periods for at least twelve months.'

Ten years, I thought, I'm not sure I could put with this for ten years.

The doctor continued, 'What we are going to do is order an ultrasound scan of your pelvic area to make sure everything is okay. I'll refer you for that today, and you should get an appointment soon.'

'Thank you, Doctor.'

'That's okay, Charlotte. You should receive it soon,' Doctor James replied.

We hung up. Well, that was a first step. I had never accepted perimenopausal or menopausal problems before. I hoped it was nothing more serious.

Sebastian came back from his training and went to the kitchen to get a protein drink. I followed him into the kitchen

'I called the doctor, babe.'

'That is great, Charlie. What did he say?'

'He said it could be menopausal, but he is going to refer me for a scan to be on the safe side.'

'Your doctor is brilliant. He doesn't mess about, Charlie, that's what you want.'

Sebastian put his arms around me. 'You'll be fine, babe,' and he kissed me on the head.

I smiled back at him.

'I've got an idea,' he said.

'What's that?' I asked.

'Let's do a theme by country for the next few days and dress and cook food to the theme for a laugh,' he said.

'What do you mean?'

Sebastian explained, 'Well let's say we do an American theme; we could dress up as cowboy and cowgirl and cook burgers and ribs.'

'Hmmm that sounds interesting, Sebastian.'

He held me in his arms. 'Weather isn't brilliant this week; let's say we start off with Italian tonight, and we both get in the kitchen?'

'That sounds great; it'll be a laugh.'

Sebastian winked at me as he walked off. 'I'm going for a shower, Charlie; feel free to join me.'

I hadn't had any bleeding this morning, so wasn't sure whether to tempt it. Sod it, I thought, let's go for it. I followed upstairs, where Sebastian was already in the shower. I undressed and walked into the bathroom to join Sebastian. I couldn't remember the last time we'd had a shower together.

I stepped into the shower and closed the door behind me. Sebastian pulled me close to him.

'You look good, babe,' he whispered as he pulled me even closer.

We stood under the shower as Sebastian kissed me on the neck. It felt sexy with the water running down our bodies and the room steaming up from the hot water. I lathered some shower gel onto my hands and started to massage Sebastian's back while he continued to kiss me. Sebastian then lathered some shower gel on his hands and massaged and lathered my breasts. He slowly moved his hand down to my virginal area and slowly rubbed his hand between my legs. He gradually pushed one of his fingers inside me.

'Is that good, babe?' he asked.

I kissed him on the lips whilst moving my hand to his penis, which was already hard.

'That's lovely,' I said.

We both carried on touching each other for a few more minutes.

'I want to be inside you,' Sebastian said.

He took his finger from inside me. 'Turn around and place your palms on the wall.'

I did exactly as he asked. Sebastian was in control this time.

'Lean towards the wall babe and slightly bend your knees for me.'

Again, I followed Sebastian's instructions. I was very wet and excited to see what he was going to do next. The water and lather were running down my body, making my skin feel soft.

He kissed me on the back of the neck. 'I'm going to take you from the back.'

His penis was hard and sticking in my back. I leant over more while he guided his penis between my legs, slowly pushing it inside me. We both started to moan, and it sounded echoey in the shower. As Sebastian pushed harder, he put his arms around me and slowly massaged my breast.

'Oh, Charlie, that's so good.'

We hadn't had sex doggy style for years in the shower; it was exciting, we were experimenting with all sorts of sex positions during the lockdown.

Sebastian was so turned on, he shouted, 'I'm coming, I'm coming,' and he moaned loud.

On that, he pushed his penis so hard inside me, we were both breathing heavily. I knew at that moment he had come. We didn't move for about a minute until Sebastian pulled his penis from inside me. I stood straight and turned around to face him. He gave me a brief kiss on the lips and put his arms around me.

'You okay?'

I looked at him and smiled. 'Yes.'

We both lathered and finished off in the shower.

The rest of the day was peaceful. We cooked an Italian meal for dinner and had a lovely date night.

The next couple of weeks continued the same. We cooked some lovely food, different cuisines from different countries. We tried American, Chinese, French, Spanish, and Indian food. We had so much fun and laughter together and far too much alcohol. The sex also continued; we tried all sorts of positions and places. We had sex in the kitchen, the lounge, on the stairs, in the office. and the bedroom.

I started my period on Tuesday 9th June, a few days late. My period only lasted five days this month, which I didn't moan about. It allowed me more sexual time with Sebastian!

We still had weekly Zoom parties with the kids. We enjoyed them, and it was wonderful to see them and catch up. The kids also texted or called every other day to check on us. If only they knew what we were up to! We agreed a date on the Zoom to meet in the garden, we could do this from the 1st of June. The weather wasn't forecast particularly good, and with work commitments for the kids, we decided to all meet on Saturday 20th June for a garden party. Sebastian and I were so excited that we had set a date to see the kids. We hadn't seen them since before lockdown, and they had both worked so hard. We loved and missed them so much and very proud of the work they were both doing.

CHAPTER 18

The Scan

It was Monday the 15th of June when a letter from the hospital arrived. I dreaded opening it but eventually hyped myself up to it. It was an appointment for an ultrasound scan for Wednesday 24 June. At least I knew I wouldn't be on my period and hoped that I wouldn't have any intermittent bleeding.

I showed the letter to Sebastian.

'That was quick, hun. At least you will get things checked,' he said. 'I'll feel better when I know you're okay.'

'Me too, babe,' I replied. 'I'm so scared; it says that the first part will be an ultrasound and the second part will be an internal.'

'Charlie, what are you worried about?'

'Well, it's the internal I don't fancy.'

Sebastian laughed. 'You've had two kids, Charlie, and all what we've been up to lately, you're worried about an internal?'

'It's okay for you, you're not the one having it done.'

'I know, I know, you'll be fine. I'll come with you if you like,' he said.

'I don't think you can. I think because of the pandemic I have to go on my own. They said they will call me with a Covid questionnaire the day before.'

'Look let's not worry about it for now.'

Today was the first day non-essential shops could open. I watched Lorraine on TV and saw big queues for people to shop in stores. It was nice to see it, but I didn't feel the need to venture out. I couldn't queue for an hour without wanting a pee, the joys of getting older.

Also, there was a scheme introduced for the self-employed to claim a salary on their income based on previous HMRC income submissions. I helped Sebastian submit his claim online. Surprisingly enough, on the website after filling in the form it stated how much he was entitled to, and it was in Sebastian's account within five working days. It had taken a long time for the government to announce something for the self-employed, but I must admit the claim was processed much faster than I expected.

Summer, Chris, and Mitch were coming over on Saturday to see us, we were so excited; we hadn't seen them since lockdown. I hadn't told them about my scan and didn't want to mention it or worry them.

Sebastian reminded me, 'We'll see the kids this weekend, babe.'

'I know, I'm so excited to see them.'

'Shall we get the BBQ out in the garden?' Sebastian asked.

'Yes, that will be lovely. I know Mitch likes his meat like you. Summer, Chris, and I will have a bit of meat with some salad,' I replied.

'I can't wait to see them, Charlie.'

'Me neither, babe. I've missed them so much. They've worked so hard through this. We've been lucky, we've both been furloughed and had the time to ourselves and luckily not had symptoms of Covid.'

Sebastian kissed me on the head. 'I know, babe, that's why we'll make the weekend special when we see them. We'll spoil them all.'

Looking forward to the weekend was exciting and planning the food we would cook. Again, Sebastian and I had great sex throughout the week. We couldn't keep our hands off each other. He made me feel so loved and cared for.

Sebastian and I spent Thursday 18th June and Friday 19th June cleaning up the garden ready for meeting up with the kids on the Saturday. We went food shopping on the Friday to get some food and drink ready for seeing them the next day. Again, we had to queue, and it took twice as long. I hated queueing, and it made shopping more of a chore rather than enjoyment.

Saturday was here before we knew it. Summer and Chris arrived about 2.00 pm. I looked at Summer and cried; it had been so long since we had seen each other. Summer also filled with tears. Sebastian was so emotional too; his baby was here at last. We sat and talked about their experiences over the past few months.

'I eventually got a Covid test done at work, and it showed that I have already had it,' she said.

'Oh my god,' Sebastian said, 'so you had it without knowing?'

'Apparently so, yes, but I think a lot of nurses have had it,' Summer replied.

'She's lucky, Charlie, that she didn't get any bad symptoms,' Chris added.

Sebastian and I nodded.

On that note, we heard the back gate open, and Mitch shouted, 'Hello, everyone; it's only me.'

My heart filled; it was Mitch.

He walked in the garden, dressed very smartly holding a girl's hand.

He blew me a kiss. 'Mom. this is Natasha.'

'Hi, Natasha, take a seat.'

I noticed she was a very pretty girl. Then I thought, must be serious for Mitch to bring a girl to meet us. They sat in the garden chatting to Summer and Chris. Sebastian went to get some drinks from the kitchen; I followed.

'Nice girl,' Sebastian said.

'Err, yes, where does he get it from?' I laughed.

'He takes after me, Charlie, you are beautiful, and I knew I'd met the one when we were young, remember that first day at college?'

We laughed and went back outside with the drinks.

Summer told us how bad it had been on the hospital and that they had lost a key worker to Covid-19. Mitch told us how mad it had been in the bank providing financial support to businesses. Sebastian and I had been completely oblivious to all of this through lockdown; we had been furloughed and lived life on our own.

Natasha seemed a very nice girl. There was chemistry between them. It was revealed that they knew each other through work, and from what I could gather, Natasha and Mitch had stayed together at Mitch's through lockdown.

As we were eating, Summer pipped up, 'We have something to tell you.'

'What is it, Summer?' Sebastian asked.

She held Chris's hand. 'I'm pregnant.'

It was silent for a minute. I looked at Sebastian, and I saw he had a tear in his eye.

Sebastian picked up his glass. 'Oh, Summer, that is great news. I'll drink to that.'

Sebastian and I held hands with joy. It was the best news we had received.

I filled with tears, but for a different reason this time. 'I can't believe I'm going to be a nanny and your dad a grandad.'

Summer laughed. 'Indeed. I cannot wait. I'm only a few weeks, Mom, so if we can keep it low key at the moment until I'm three months and had my scan.'

'Of course, Summer; we won't say a word to anyone.'

Sebastian and I were so delighted. The news of a baby on the way and that Mitch was in a relationship, we couldn't have wished for anything better. We all felt so close as a family again; we had missed them so much. We ate and drank a lot to celebrate, apart from Summer, who didn't drink but had lots of hot drinks and food. Sebastian and I were so proud of the kids.

When it was time to leave, we blew kisses at them. It had felt like a lifetime since we had seen them and spent time together as a family.

Summer whispered across to me, 'You'll see us on Sunday, Mom, for Father's Day. We'll pop over.'

Mitch had a tear in his eye when he left. He blew a kiss to us, saying, 'I love you Mom and Dad so much. This lockdown has made me grow up and realise what's important in my life.'

Mitch winked. 'I can't wait to be an uncle.'

When they left, Sebastian and I sat and spoke about the news. Blimey we were going to become grandparents, and Mitch looked all loved up. We were the happiest parents ever.

Throughout the remainder of June, things continued the same. Sebastian and I were so loved up and enjoyed our sexual encounters. We had sex in all sorts of positions and some great oral sex using toys and whips.

I checked my work emails regularly, but the message was still the same; all staff were furloughed until further notice.

Sunday 21st June was another great day. The kids came over for Father's Day. Sebastian was overjoyed. Natasha wasn't with Mitch. He said that she had gone to see her parents. She did call him though, and we heard 'Love you too, babe.' This sounded serious!

Sebastian had cards from both and cases of ales, chocolates, and aftershave. Whilst I was in the kitchen preparing some food, I looked out the window at them. Sebastian was so enjoying spending time with the kids, the smiles on all their faces were to treasure. All the visiting from the kids took my mind off the scan.

On Tuesday 23rd June, I got a call from the hospital to confirm my appointment. They ran through a series of Covid questions such as had I had a cough or temperate on the past twenty-four hours, had I been asked to self-isolate, and lots of other questions. They then told me that on arrival, I should enter and wait for my temperature to be taken and to put on a face mask I would be offered. I must admit the scan itself was worrying me without all the other additional Covid things. I was also told to make sure I had a full bladder.

The following day, I left at about 12.00 noon; my appointment was 12.40 pm. I drank loads of water. I thought I was going to burst. On arrival, I was given a mask to put on, and I had to stand in a square for my temperature to be taken. I was then directed where to go for the scan. My heartbeat was going ten to the dozen. I had butterflies in my tummy. I had been sick on the morning worrying about the appointment.

After arriving at the department and checking in, they asked me to strip down into a gown to my underwear in a dressing cubical and put all my clothes in a locker. I felt a bit claustrophobic in the face mask and not well. I waited in the waiting area until called through. I looked at my mobile; there was a text from Sebastian.

'Good luck, babe, call me as soon as you come out. I love you lots.'

I text back, 'Thanks, babe, love you too.'

The nurse in charge called me through and asked me to confirm my name, address, and date of birth. She then got me to lay on the bed ready. Soon after, a doctor appeared and explained the scan to me.

The doctor started by explaining that she was going to put some gel on my pelvic area to look what was going on. I seemed okay with this. She performed the scan and looked at a computer screen pressing buttons whilst moving the scanning devise across my pelvic area.

She then stopped and looked at me.

'Okay, Mrs Dyson, we need to perform the second part of the examination, which is an internal.'

'Do you need to do this?' I asked. 'Do you not have enough information from the scan?'

'It's best we do it, Mrs Dyson. I couldn't see your ovaries clear, and this will give us a much clearer picture. You have come this far to be checked.'

'I'm dying for a wee,' I said as an excuse.

The doctor laughed. 'I would let you go to the toilet first, Mrs Dyson.'

'Do I need a clamp or anything?' I asked.

The doctor laughed again. 'Not at all; this is much easier than a smear.'

I thought about it for a few seconds. 'Okay, let's see how we get on.'

I was asked to go into the toilet to empty my bladder, remove my pants, and wipe all the gel off my pelvic area. I was a complete wreck; the mask didn't help as it made it harder to breathe, more so when I had a panicky feeling, and I struggled to talk.

When I arrived back in the room, I was asked to sit on the end of the bed with my feet on a chair at the end of the bed. The doctor showed me a kind of wand attached to a computer.

'Okay, Mrs Dyson, this is what we will slowly insert inside you to take a look. It is very well lubricated so as to enter easily.'

The doctor slowly lowered the bed so my legs were elevated with my feet still on the chair. She lifted my gown slightly and slowly enter the wand type thing inside me.

'Are you okay,' she asked.

I took deep breaths. 'Yes I'm fine.'

She slowly moved the instrument around whilst taking pictures on the computer. It didn't hurt as much as a smear, just slightly when she moved it from side to side.

After a few minutes, the doctor said, 'Okay, we're all done, Mrs Dyson. I'm going to slowly bring it out.'

I was so relieved it was all over; it wasn't as bad as I expected.

'You'll receive your results in a few days to your GP,' she said.

I cleaned myself up, got dressed, and left for home. It was such a relief when it was done.

When I got home, Sebastian was waiting for me. He looked so worried.

'You've been ages, babe; how did it go?'

I smiled. 'It was okay, not as bad as I thought it would be. I had to have that internal thing where they inserted something to look inside.'

'Are you okay, though?' Sebastian asked.

'Yes, they said the results would be with my GP in a few days.'

Sebastian put his arms around me and kissed me on the head.

I joked. 'I tell you something, the thing they inserted for the internal was huge. Next time we have sex, I'll be asking you where it is, is it in.'

Sebastian laughed 'Trust you. We can try it later if you'd like.'

That evening, Sebastian cooked my favourite again—cheese and potato pie with spareribs. I thoroughly enjoyed it and relaxed, relieved the appointment was over. We snuggled on the same sofa on the evening to watch TV. He didn't try anything that evening, which I was pleased about as I felt a little sore.

It was Friday the 26th of June when I got a call from my doctor. My mobile rang, and I could see it was the doctor. My heart started racing as I answered the call.

'Is this Charlotte Dyson I'm speaking to?' he asked.

'Yes, Doctor.'

He asked me to confirm a few details for identification, then he went on to say, 'Now, Charlotte, we have the results back from your ultrasound scan, and it's good news. There is nothing untoward, just a problem that we can treat with medication. I believe it is menopausal problems you must be suffering with. It is up to you if you want medication to help with that?' the doctor asked.

'That's great news, Doctor. I had worked myself up that something was wrong but pleased to hear not. I'll start by trying to deal with the menopause myself, and I'll have a think if I need any medical help,' I replied.

'That's the best thing, Charlotte. See how you get on and how you're feeling. Only you will know if you want some medication to help.'

'Thank you, Doctor,' I replied.

I was so relieved to hear that everything was okay. I had worked myself up in believing that something was wrong.

After the call, I shouted to Sebastian and told him the news; he held me tightly.

'That is the best news ever, Charlie. I'm so pleased. We've had some good news over the past week with Summer, Mitch, and you; let's hope we're turning a corner.'

I felt so relieved. I cracked open a bottle of prosecco to celebrate.

'A bit early, babe,' Sebastian said.

'Never too early, we're celebrating life.'

'Well, we have been drinking a lot through lockdown so why break the habit now.' He laughed.

I poured us a drink to celebrate our good news.

CHAPTER 19

MEMORIES

The first few weeks of July were great. Sebastian and I spent time having long walks and reminiscing about our marriage and the kids. We were both so relieved that my ultrasound scan was okay and so excited to hear the news of a baby from Summer. I couldn't imagine us being grandparents. We didn't feel or look old enough! Life was good between us.

One day early July, the weather was hot.

'Shall we go for a walk over the fields, Charlie, and take a picnic with us?' Sebastian asked.

We hadn't had a picnic out since the kids were young. The last time was at Drayton Manor when we took the kids and sat on the grass to eat some lunch.

'That sounds exciting; we haven't done that since the kids were little.' I smiled.

We were both excited, like two little kids. It was something different for us.

'I'll get the cool bag out the garage, if you want to start to make some food for us to take.' Sebastian winked as he walked past me.

I opened the fridge and grabbed the cheese, ham, and butter and made us some nice butties and wrapped them in some foil. I also got some crisps and sausage rolls to take. I grabbed some pop and two plastic glasses and put them on the side to take with us. Sebastian had been ages getting the cool bag, so I went to the garage to look for him. I might have guessed; he had opened the garage door up to let some light in and was talking to the neighbour about lockdown and going back to work. He turned and spotted me in the garage. I didn't want to get caught chatting, so I shouted quickly, 'Just going upstairs to get changed, Sebastian. Don't be too long as we're going out.'

He smiled back at me. I decided to put a white top on with straps, shorts, and some sliders; it was too hot for anything else. When I arrived back downstairs, Sebastian had cleaned the cool bag out and packed everything.

'Great teamwork, Charlie.' He smiled.

'It is indeed,' I replied. 'I've got us a blanket to sit on.'

Sebastian wore a pair of navy shorts and white adidas top with adidas trainers. He looked very handsome and muscular.

'Right, let's go then,' he said. 'Are you going to be okay to walk in those flip flops? It's a good twenty-minute walk.'

'I'm fine,' I replied, 'and they're not flip flops they are sliders.'

Sebastian nodded as he picked up the cool bag as if to say whatever. We started off on our walk along some lanes and headed to a beautiful field that backed on to a farm. He held my hand all the way, not sure if it was because he wanted to or if it was to make sure I walked at his pace with my sliders on. We talked all the way about our last picnic and visit to Drayton Manor. We had such good memories of when the kids were little. Before we knew it, we were at the field. We opened the gate to the field and found a spot where no one could see us. There was only us there, anyway.

I lay down a blanket, and we sat on it. The sun was scorching. I could feel my skin starting to burn and turn red.

'Fancy a drink, babe?' Sebastian asked.

'Yea, I do. I feel a bit dehydrated.'

Sebastian opened the cool bag and got two bottles of beer out and opened them with an opener on his keyring.

'I didn't know you'd packed beer, Mr Dyson. I put some pop out.' I laughed.

'I know you did, Mrs Dyson. I put the pop back in the fridge,' he replied as he passed me a bottle.

'Do you want a glass, babe?' he asked as he took a swig out of his bottle.

'No, I'm fine with the bottle, tastes better.'

It was lovely and peaceful. We sat chatting, drinking our beer. Sebastian mainly talked about work and how he was looking forward to going back as soon as the gyms reopened. I couldn't say I was looking forward to going back to work. I was enjoying our time together. It was beautiful to look out over the farm field; it was a light green colour, almost yellow, not sure if it was corn.

'This is so lovely, Charlie, just you and I sitting here.'

'Do you want another drink?' he asked

'What? You have more beer in the cool bag?'

'Hmmmm, even better than that, babe. I have your favourite,' he said as he pulled out a bottle of prosecco.

'What else have you got in that bag?' I asked as I leant over to look in.

Sebastian pulled the bag away, laughing. 'Nothing for you. It's a secret; it's pandora's box. What's on the sandwiches?'

I joked. 'I'm not telling you. It's a secret; you'll have to wait and see.'

Sebastian laughed and poured me a glass of prosecco; it didn't take long for me to drink it. I lay back on the blanket with my arms reaching up over my head, looking up at the clear blue sky.

Sebastian lay next to me. 'Do you remember the first time we kissed, Charlie?'

'Of course, I do.' I laughed.

'You were so young, sweet, and innocent.'

'And I'm not now?' I asked.

'You are, my dear, come here,' he replied as he leant on his side and pulled me to him for a kiss. He kissed me a couples of times, pecks on the lips, then kissed me again for a long time putting his tongue in my mouth. I closed my eyes as we snogged. I would never have dreamt of doing this at our age. Sebastian slowly moved his right hand down onto my breast and started to feel it.

'You've got lovely big breasts, Charlie,' he whispered as he started to kiss my neck.

I moved his hand away. 'Someone might come.'

Sebastian whispered, 'There's no one here. Let's have some fun and a sense of adventure,' as he carried on kissing my neck and moved his hand back on my right breast. We were both a little tipsy, giggling like kids. Sebastian started to move from kissing my neck to my shoulder, moving my strap down on my top. I started to feel excited, more so because we were outside. He then moved to kissing my collarbone whilst still feeling my breast. It wasn't long before he moved down to my right breast and pulled my top down so that my breast was in the open. I hadn't got a bra on; it was too hot. He kissed my breast whilst still feeling it with his hand and slowly moved to the nipple where he sucked and bit hard on it. I was so sexually aroused; I could feel the wetness of my citreous.

Whilst still sucking on my nipple, Sebastian moved his hand between my legs and started to feel me.

'Do you want it, Charlie?' he whispered.

I moaned. 'Yes, right now, here.'

He undid the button and zip on my shorts and slid his hand inside them, feeling in between my legs. He pushed my legs wide open with his leg.

'Open your legs wide for me, babe. You're so wet.'

Sebastian moved his forefinger up and down my vaginal area whilst moving his thumb in a circular position. I had silk pants on, which made the feeling even better. They seemed to allow his fingers to move and slide about much easier.

'I love your big nipples, Charlie; they turn me on so much,' he whispered as he bit harder.

Sebastian then moved his hand to the side of my pants and slid his hand inside them. He moved his finger up and down my vagina, then gradually pushed one finger in. His head moved up from my breast where he kissed me intimately on the lips.

'I' going to make you come, babe,' he said as he slid a second finger inside.

The movement of Sebastian's fingers got faster and faster, moving back and forth. I moaned even louder and started to tense. My body started to shudder, and I got a warm fuzzy feeling in my body.

'I'm coming, babe,' I shouted.

It was like a release and exposition of pleasure. I lay looking at the blue sky, my heart was pounding, and my breathing was still heavy.

'I love you, Charlie.' Sebastian kissed me on the forehand whilst moving his hand out of my pants and shorts. He lay back down off his side onto his back next to me. I could see he had a hard on, his penis was bulging out of his shorts. I pulled my top back up over my breast and turned on my side towards Sebastian. I kissed him on the lips and rubbed my one hand between his legs.

'You're so hard, babe. Do you want some fun?'

'Play with me, Charlie, and suck me.'

I slowly undid his shorts and pulled them down slightly. Sebastian didn't have any boxers on today. I put my hands around his penis and moved it up and down, slowly masturbating him. Sebastian put his hands up over his head, looked down at me, and said softly, 'That's lovely, babe, kiss my balls.'

I moved my body down to his bottom half and started to kiss and feel his balls. I licked them gently, slowing moving my mouth to his penis. I sucked on his penis very slowly whist still masturbating his penis with my hand. He was wet. I could taste it in my mouth. I shifted my body over so that I was in the middle of his legs. I carried on sucking his penis slowly and feeling his balls and penis with my hands. Sebastian started to breathe heavier; the heavier he breathed, the faster I sucked. I knew he was turned on and nearly ready to come. He grabbed my head and pushed it back and forth to guide the movement faster.

'I love your mouth around my cock.'

As I sucked harder, his body started to tense, and he moaned louder; louder than I'd ever known.

'I'm coming, babe, suck me hard,' he moaned loudly.

I put his penis deeper into my mouth. I knew Sebastian had come. I got a wet sensation in my mouth. As I moved my mouth from his penis, I got dribbles down my chin and on my breast.

'That was the best ever blow job, babe.'

'It's all over me.' I laughed as I sat up.

Sebastian reached for the cool bag whilst still lying down, got a tissue, and handed it me.

'Did you plan this?' I asked.

'I told you, you have no idea what is in pandora's box.' He giggled

I wiped my mouth and chest with the tissue and passed some tissue to Sebastian to wipe himself clean. He zipped his shorts up and lay back down. I lay beside him, and we both held hands, looking at the sky.

Suddenly, I thought of the rape that had happened to me when I was younger. I had never told Sebastian about the ordeal and what I was made to do. It must have been the impulse of having oral sex outside in the open, probably also the fact that I was tipsy. My emotions came over me very strongly, and I started to re-live the ordeal as I looked at the blue sky. A tear ran down my face. I hadn't felt like this before with Sebastian; it was my secret that I never wanted to talk about, and all of sudden, the memories came flooding back.

Sebastian looked over at me. 'Shall we have some lunch, babe?'

He noticed I had tears. 'He sat up. "Are you upset, Charlie? Have I done something?'

I wiped my eyes. 'No, Sebastian, I'm fine. I think I've got sun lotion in my eyes from all the sweating we've done. I must have rubbed them.'

'Put on your sunglasses, Charlie; that will help,' he said.

'Yes, I will.' I reached over for my little shoulder bag and got my sunglasses to put on. They were big Calvin Klein glasses that Sebastian had bought me at the airport many years ago.

'Right, shall we have some munch, Charlie?'

'Oh yes, this is my surprises now.' I laughed

Sebastian put the cool bag in the middle of us, and we munched on sausage rolls, sandwiches, and more alcohol.

We laughed again and giggled like teenagers.

'I love you, Charlie, and so proud we are going to be grandparents. You've done well bringing up the kids. This is where we can enjoy having grandkids to stay but can give them back when we've had enough.'

'Yes, so true, Sebastian. We can enjoy our lives whist seeing our newly addition to the family.'

'Charlie, I want us to think about retiring at fifty-five and doing some travelling and spending time with the grandchildren or child, I should say at the moment. We should start planning for that now,' Sebastian suggested.

'Wouldn't that be nice, Sebastian. I hope we will be in a position to do that.'

'We will: trust me,' he replied.

After eating and drinking everything we had, we packed up for home. We walked home holding hands just had we'd done walking there. On the way home, I still couldn't get the thought out of my head of the ordeal when I was younger, the oral sex outside had triggered the memory, one that I never wanted to remember.

Chapter 20
Coming Out of Lockdown

So eventually the dreaded email came through from work I was expecting with a date to return to work.

The email stated that a deep clean of the office and social distances measures was currently being implemented at work and we were advised to return on Monday 20th July at 9.00 am and to be as close to the time as possible where an update would be given.

Boris Johnson had also announced that gyms, leisure centres, and indoor pools were all allowed to open from Saturday 25 July. They would have to follow strict new guidelines, such as introducing timed bookings for workouts and restrictions on showering.

Sebastian was so pleased he could go back to the gym. He already started taking calls from clients and planning his diary.

The weekend of the 17th of July was fabulous. We arranged for our friends Gemma and John to come stay over for the weekend; we hadn't seen them since just prior to the lockdown.

We'd arranged for them to arrive on the Friday afternoon about midday to make a weekend of it. As usual they arrived on time, five minutes to midday. They were so pleased to see us, and they hugged us so hard.

'We haven't seen anybody, darling, since we were last here,' Gemma said.

She went on to say, 'We've had to protect our son, as you know he is vulnerable; we've lived in a little bubble with carers coming in and shopping delivered. None of us have worked, Charlie, so it's just been us.'

'I bet you've enjoyed it just being the two of you, Gemma, and not having to work,' I said.

'No, not at all, we haven't. As you know, our privacy in the home has gone with having carers 24/7, to add to that, we've not been able to go out in case we picked up the virus and bought it home. We love staying away in hotels to get some time alone but we've not even been able to do that,' she replied.

'And to add to that, some of the carers on the rota have been vulnerable or having to self-isolate, so we have had to cover their shifts.'

'Gosh, Gemma, what a nightmare for you both.'

'I know, at least we can get out now, but we are choosing our bubbles and you are one of them,' Gemma said.

They looked very well, nice sun tans and very chilled. As usual, they bought some nice food for us to cook.

Gemma always had dark hair like me, but this time, it was blonde. It made her look very different. It suited her with tanned skin.

'You've gone lighter, Gemma, with your hair,' I said.

'Ohh, yes, it was driving me mad. The grey was coming through, and I didn't want to keep doing my roots every few weeks, so I went lighter all over. The grey routes blend in now; look.'

Gemma lent forward, bowing her head whilst pulling her hair to one side on the top.

'You can hardly see the roots, they blend in,' I said.

'Yes, that's what I thought. The sun has also lightened it. You don't have any grey Charlie, have you coloured it?' Gemma asked.

'I've picked a few colours up from the supermarket and been putting those on. My hairdresser is coming next week. Yippee! She will do my all over colour and a cut. She's also going to cut Sebastian's hair; look how it's grown. I wanted to chop it, but he wouldn't let me.'

Gemma laughed. 'Typical Sebastian not letting you cut it! I've got my hair booked in for a few weeks' time. I might go back dark again.'

Sebastian piped up, 'There's no way, Charlie, I'm letting you near my hair with scissors, you'd be at my throat.'

I nodded and tutted.

'Right, Charlie, shall we start with a brunch breakfast and a glass of prosecco?' Gemma suggested.

'That sounds good to me, Gemma,' I replied.

Sebastian smiled and winked at me. 'What a perfect way to start the weekend.'

I winked back at him. 'Absolutely, let's go for it.'

John cooked the perfect brunch consisting of eggs, bacon, beans, tomatoes, and mushrooms with toast. The weather was glorious, so I laid the table outside to eat.

'Cheers and to good health,' John said.

We all held our glasses up and clanged our glasses to good health and all getting through the other end. This was the first time we had spent any time with friends, and it was so lovely. The brunch was gorgeous; we all gobbled it down. The gents offered to wash up after, or should I say, fill the dishwasher!

John and Sebastian were soon back outside, the weather was so hot.

'Shall we put on our bikini's, Charlie?' Gemma asked.

It was rather hot, so I agreed. We went upstairs and got changed. We met again at the top of the stairs in our bikini's.

'You look wonderful, Charlie,' Gemma commented.

'I look fat. I think I've put the Covid stone on.' I laughed.

Gemma laughed. 'There's nothing to you; don't get paranoid. If anything, look at me.'

I paid back the compliment. 'Don't be silly, Gemma, you are beautiful.'

We both appeared downstairs in front of the gentlemen in our bikini's. We put a towel on the lawn, soaked up with suntan lotion, and lay in the sun. Sebastian came over to top our glasses up occasionally.

'Top up, ladies?' he would shout.

We never denied a top up. Sometimes, he'd whisper in my ear, 'Just for you babe, enjoy.'

'So, what have you two been up to? Have you worked?' Gemma asked.

'No, we've both been furloughed. I go back to work on Monday, and as you know, the gyms open up again the week after,' I replied.

'Sebastian still looks fit, darling. What's he been doing without the gym?' Gemma asked.

'As you know, he's a fitness freak. He found it hard when the gyms first closed and went a bit depressed on me. When we knew lockdown was going to be longer than expected, he found a routine. We've done a lot of walking. Sebastian's done some running, and the neighbour has let him use their gym.'

'Oh, that's good, Charlie, plus it gave you some space while he was out.'

'Exactly that, Gemma. I thought at one point we were going to kill each other, but it turned out okay.'

'That's what we've missed. We've had no space at all from each other or even together with the carers coming in.'

'Yes, it must have been hard for you. How is Dan doing?'

'He's okay, Charlie, the carers are good, and he has enjoyed us being around more.'

'I'm pleased to hear that.'

'So, what else you two been up to? Gemma asked.

I wasn't going to discuss with Gemma that we had been up to all sorts of sexual activity, a bit like 50 Shades of Grey lockdown!

'Nothing much, gardening, cooking, cleaning, sunbathing, the usual stuff,' I said.

'Same as us. Are the kids okay?'

'They're great, thanks, Gemma. They have been over a couple of times, both been busy with work. Summer said it's been busy in the hospital with Covid patients. We did worry about her.'

'It's been awful on the TV about people who have suffered with Covid and been in hospital.'

'We've tried not to watch a lot of it, Gemma; we watched the update from Government each day, and that's it. It's all been too depressing and upsetting. We even gave up watching the Prime Minster updates in the end.'

'Hmmm, I know what you mean, Charlie.'

'oh, and I haven't told you. Mitch turned up with a girl.'

'No way, since when and how in lockdown? What a dark horse.'

'He said he knew her from work, and they had been spending time together through lockdown. As you know, he is a bit of a charmer, never been short of women. She's a very pretty girl, long blonde hair, big boobs, you know the type Mitch would go for.'

'I bet there's been some right sexual activity going on there in lockdown. Good for him.' Gemma laughed. 'I don't know who Mitch takes after.'

I smiled and blushed a little. If only she knew what we'd been up to. I chose not to mention Summer being pregnant. She had asked us not to tell anyone until she was three months and had her first scan.

We spent the rest of the afternoon chatting and updating each other. It was so lovely to see friends again. We drank lots of alcohol, so much that I went to bed at 8.00 pm not remembering the last few hours.

I woke up around 8.00 am on Saturday with a banging headache. This was late for me, albeit I was still the first up. I took some headache tablets and a dioralyte to get rid of my headache before the others got up. Everyone else seemed fine; it was just me!

John and Sebastian cooked breakfast while I lay on the sofa feeling sorry for myself, chatting to Gemma.

John popped his head round. 'Bucks fizz for everyone with breakfast.'

'Yes, lovely John,' Gemma replied.

The thought right now of prosecco made me feel sick.

'I don't know if I can drink just yet, John. It's only ten o clock.'

Sebastian heard me and shouted, 'You like your prosecco, Charlie, not like you to refuse a drink.'

I heard him say to John, 'I think she's menopausal,' and they both laughed.

It annoyed me that Sebastian had gone back to the menopause again and the fact that he had said that to John. He hadn't mentioned anything for weeks.

'I heard that Sebastian,' I shouted. He didn't respond.

Shortly after, the breakfast and bucks fizz was laid out on the table, and we all sat to eat.

'You like your prosecco, Charlie,' Sebastian said.

'I know what I like. I'll have one shortly,' I snarled back. I was still annoyed with him.

'Are you in the menopause then, Charlie?' Gemma asked.

God, now we are on the subject, all because Sebastian mentioned it.

'Not sure, Gemma, I've had a few problems, but I'm okay.' I looked at Sebastian .'I will have that prosecco, please.'

He poured me a glass and added a small amount of orange juice. He knew he had pissed me off.

'What problems, Charlie, you had?'

'Only with my monthly cycle, Gemma, a bit late or early here and there.'

'You should see the doctor,' Gemma suggested.

I didn't want to go into or talk about the scan I had.

'Do you have hot sweats and mood swings?' Gemma asked.

This definitely wasn't a topic I wanted to talk about.

'No, Gemma, I don't, so not sure if I am menopausal,' I replied.

Sebastian glared at me, and I glared back.

'It's okay. I'm only asking because I know a consultant who offers all kinds of support and natural medication for the menopause. I have a few friends who have used her, and they were impressed. I will go to her when I get to the menopause,' Gemma said.

I reluctantly replied, 'Thanks, Gemma, leave her details in case I need her in the future.'

We finished our breakfast, cleared up, and sat out in the garden for the day. The weather wasn't as hot today, but it was still rather warm.

Like the day before, we drank lots of alcohol. Things were a bit frosty between Sebastian and me. I was still annoyed with him from the morning.

I asked Gemma and John, 'What's your thoughts on a second lockdown?'

John was the first to answer. 'Well, it's like this. The virus hasn't gone anywhere; it's still here. It will be a few weeks before we know any impact from any restrictions being lifted and then, of course, there was all these riots. That hasn't helped.'

Gemma jumped in. 'And then we go into the colder months. Without a vaccine, it is inevitable we will get a second wave, darling.'

'Are you stocking up again?' I asked.

'We've still got dried food like pasta in the house just in case. If it happens, it will be a long winter.'

'I hope not, Gemma. I'm self-employed, and it was a long wait to get some money from the government,' Sebastian replied.

John commented, flapping his arms around. 'It's not a case of will we get a second; it's a case of when. Will it then be worse than the first? Will we have regional lockdowns? Nobody knows; it's new, and we bloody need a vaccine soon. Anyway, what do I know? It's only my opinion.'

'I think everyone is thinking the same, John, that it's inevitable we'll get a second wave. I hope it's not as bad as the first, especially for poor Summer at the hospital,' I replied.

It was quiet for a minute. 'Right, let's change the subject and enjoy the weekend. Gent's get us a top up,' I said.

We drank and ate for the rest of the day. John cooked some delicious hot dogs with caramelised onions. As usual, I did my party trick and fell asleep on the sofa. I woke up about 2.00 am freezing in the lounge in darkness.

I managed to get upstairs to the bedroom. I undressed and threw all my clothes on the floor. I just wanted my bed. I disturbed Sebastian in doing so.

'Oh, here you are, babe. What time is it?' he asked.

'It's 2.00 am. Why didn't you wake me for bed?' I asked.

'I tried; you were comatised,' he replied.

I didn't reply and closed my eyes. I was too tired to talk. It didn't take long for me to fall back off to sleep, and I slept through the night.

I woke about 7.00 am, which again was late for me. Sebastian was already awake lying on his back, stretching his arms out.

'Did you sleep well, babe?' he asked.

I still felt sleepy, 'Hmmmm, yes, thank you.'

CHAPTER 21
THE LAST TIME

This was my last day before back to work, Sunday 19th July 2020. I lay in bed thinking about how it would be back in the office and what restrictions would be in place. It'll be strange getting up and ready for work.

Sebastian got out of bed and went to the bathroom for a pee. As usual, he was naked. He still never slept in nightwear. After five minutes as he walked back from the bathroom, I noted his penis was hanging semi hard. His body looked very tanned and muscular. Why do most men wake up with a hard on, I thought!

Sebastian looked at me as he got back into bed. 'Penny for your thoughts.'

'Just thinking about work tomorrow and how it will be.'

'Well, don't think too much. Come here, and I'll take your mind off it,' he said as he put his arm around and pulled me towards him on my side. I was also naked in bed too, my clothes from the previous day still lay on the floor. He started to kiss me on the lips, his breathing got heavier.

I pulled away. 'We can't now, Sebastian. We've got visitors, and they'll hear us.'

He pulled himself on top of me and started kissing me again. 'No they won't, Charlie. We'll be quiet; let's be daring.'

He kissed me intimately for about five minutes, feeling my breasts at the same time. I had my arms around his muscular body, rubbing my hands through his hair.

'Let's get you wet,' he said as he moved from kissing my lips to my breasts for a few minutes sucking and kissing them. I started to get aroused, and my nipples hardened. Sebastian then moved farther down, kissing my stomach and abdomen slowly on the way down, finally pulling my legs open with his hands and kissing around the vaginal area. After a few minutes of kissing the tops of my legs and around my vaginal area, Sebastian started to slowly lick my vagina. He pushed my knees up and open so he could get his tongue inside me.

I felt butterflies in my body as he licked my citreous area with his tongue, licking in a circular movement. I got hotter and hotter; in fact, I started to sweat, and my breathing became heavier.

I sat up slightly. 'Sebastian, come here and make love to me. I don't want to come yet. I want us to come together.'

He moved from licking my vagina, back up to kissing my abdomen, then my stomach to my breasts, and finally my lips. I wrapped my legs around his strong body. He held my arms down above my head so that I couldn't move and kissed me slowly and intimately. I felt his penis slowly push against my vagina. I was so wet, it slipped inside me easily. We both carried on kissing intimately and breathing heavier and heavier. I started to moan out loud as he pushed his penis in and out slowly. I was conscious that our visitors were still here. I'd be so embarrassed if they heard us.

'I love you so much, Charlie,' Sebastian said as he pushed harder.

'I love you too, babe,' I said as he put his head on my shoulder and released my arms.

I put my arms around his body and dug my nails into his back, and he pushed harder and harder. We were so hot and sweating, the room was warm. The headboard knocked against the wall. I thought of the noise but couldn't stop now.

'I'm coming, babe,' he said.

I felt my body starting to shudder and felt like I was going to explode. It was great sensational feeling.

'I'm coming with you,' I said.

On that, Sebastian pushed his penis hard into me, then stopped for a few seconds before pushing hard again. He did this repeatedly three times. I knew he had come. He lay on top of me for a while after with his head on my shoulder. He then lifted his head and gave me a peck on the lips.

'Happy Sunday, Mrs Dyson, nice start to the day. I bet you're not thinking about work now?'

I smile., 'Indeed, my dear, happy Sunday. You took my mind off work.'

'That's' my girl,' he said as he lifted himself off me. 'I'll jump in the shower first if that's okay.'

'Yes, no worries.'

I got out of bed and picked my clothes up off the floor, put them into the washing basket, then showered after Sebastian. Once we were dressed, we headed downstairs. To my shock, Gemma and John were already up. I never heard them. They were sitting in the lounge with a hot drink. The lounge was underneath our bedroom. My first thought was whether they had heard us or the bed knocking, my face reddened with embarrassment.

'Hope you don't mind, darling, we made ourselves our drink,' Gemma said.

'No, not at all; help yourselves,' I replied. 'I'll get Sebastian and I one. Do you want another?'

'Wouldn't say no, Charlie,' John pipped up.

'Nor me,' Gemma replied as she passed their cups to me.

I went to the kitchen; I could still feel my face burning up wondering whether they knew we'd just had sex. Sebastian followed me.

'You look a bit red. You okay?' he asked.

'Do you think they heard us in bed?'

'Don't be daft; you worry too much. Anyway, so what if they did? We are married and in our own house.'

'Yea but it's not right when we've got visitors.'

He smacked me on the bum as he walked off back into the lounge. 'You didn't think about being a visitor that time at my mom's; you panic too much. It makes it more daring, and you loved it.'

I shook my head. Can't believe he said that, I told myself.

We drank our tea and had a wonderful, cooked breakfast together before we said our goodbyes. The weekend passed by so quickly. We hugged each other as we always do.

'It's been lovely to see you both again,' Gemma said.

John added, 'Well, we have another date in the diary for end of August. Thank you both for a great weekend.'

It was always sad to see them go; they were a good laugh, and we always had fun together.

As this was my last day before work, we had asked Summer and Mitch to come for Sunday lunch. They were due to arrive about 3.00 pm for us to eat about 4.00 pm. A bit mad, one lot of guests leave as another is due to arrive. Well, can't call Summer and Mitch guests; they still treat it like home.

I got in the kitchen and started to prep the dinner. I planned to do roast pork, mash potatoes, roast potatoes, and lots of vegetables. Sebastian and Mitch loved my Sunday roasts with lots of veg. Summer was a bit like me. I didn't mind some veg but loved mashed and roast potatoes. Sebastian and I were so excited that the kids were coming for dinner. Mitch was bringing his new girlfriend, so I needed to make an impression on my cooking.

'Can I help, Charlie, with anything?' Sebastian asked.

'If you could peel some potatoes for me, babe, that would help.'

'Sure, I can do that,' he replied.

We prepared the dinner whilst listening to a flashback to the 80s on the radio. They played some great songs that we remembered including Madonna, U2, Wham.

'Remember this,' we said to each other.

It was good memories; our college days together were fantastic; it was love at first sight for us. We loved listening to music while we were cooking. It gave us that good feel. I got the meat into cook as it needed a good two and half hours. I wanted to get the crackling nice and crunchy. I was good at doing that.

'Okay, babe, meat is in cooking. Everything else is prepared for cooking. You've done a great job. I think you deserve a glass of prosecco, fancy one?' Sebastian asked.

'I don't mind if I do,' I replied, pleased that everything was done.

Sebastian cracked open a bottle for me, and he got himself a beer.

'Cheers, my dear,' he said.

'Cheers.'

Summer and Chris arrived about quarter to three. Summer was always prompt and on time; even as a child, she always had to be at school early. We all hugged each other tight. I saw a tear fill in Sebastian's eye. Summer was Sebastian's little blued eyed baby, even though she was grown up, she was still his daddy's girl, and now having a baby of her own. They went and sat in the lounge chatting whilst I got the meat out of the oven.

'Do you want a beer, Chris?' I shouted.

'I will do thanks, Charlie. I might as well make the best of it now I have a chauffeur for the next few months,' he shouted back.

I got Chris his favourite beer out of the fridge. I knew he loved Becks in a bottle.

'Lovely, Charlie, you got my favourite beer in,' he said as I handed him the bottle.

I winked at him. Chris was a good lad. He looked after Summer. Sebastian and I approved of him.

Shortly after, a key went in the front door, and we all looked up. It was Mitch with Natasha. They walked in, kissed, and hugged us all, and sat down to join us.

'You shouldn't use your key now. You've got our own place,' Summer said, which was typical of her.

'Summer, it's our Mom and Dad, not some strangers house,' Mitch replied.

'I know, but what if they were up to something?'

'Errr, I doubt it. What at their age?' Mitch replied.

'Well, you never know,' Summer replied.

'Excuse me, kids, we are in the room,' I said.

They both smiled at each other as if to say that was Mother telling them to button it.

'I wonder if you have sex in your fifties and what it's like,' Mitch continued.

'Dunno,' Summer said. 'It might be a bit flabby.'

'Right, can we change the conversation please, and for the record I'm not fifty until September,' I said.

Mitch does it sometimes to wind me up. He is so like his father at times like this. Sebastian didn't say a word and laughed it off.

'Fifty this year, Mom. What are you going to do or what do you want to do?' Summer asked.

'I'm not sure, Summer. I'll see how things go with the coronavirus. Your dad and I were going to go away abroad, but I can't see that happening now. There's also no point arranging a party because you can't have buffets and limited to the number of guests.'

Sebastian put his arm around me. 'We'll see nearer the time. We'll do something, Charlie, even if it's a party between us.'

'How's the mother-to-be doing?' Mitch asked.

'I'm good ta, no morning sickness or anything yet,' Summer replied, holding Chris's hand.

'Any names yet?' Mitch asked.

'No, we'll wait until I'm three months, then look at names,' Summer replied.

You could see the excitement on Summer and Chris's face. Mitch loved is younger sister; he always looked out for her. Any trouble and he'd be there.

'I'm going to be a great Uncle Mitch Summer,' Mitch said holding Natasha's hand.

Summer smiled. 'Indeed, Mitch, he or she can't wait to meet you.'

I went off into the kitchen and left them to it to cut the meat and cook the rest of the dinner. The crackling was fabulous and crispy. I thought about the kids view on sex at fifty, and Summer saying it was flabby. God if they only knew what we'd been up to, we'd had the best sex ever during lockdown.

Summer soon followed in.

'Oh, Mom, look at that crackling,' she said as she picked some off the plate.

'I've been sooooo looking forward to this Sunday roast,' she went to say.

Summer then picked some meat off the plate. I tapped her hand.

'Oy, you're going to spoil your dinner; stop picking and go and sit down.'

'I'm feeding for two now, Mother.' she said.

Summer went back into the lounge to sit down. I carried on cooking and dishing up.

'Right, everyone at the table, dinner is coming,' I shouted. I could hear them all laughing amongst themselves and moving to the table. It was perfect, just like it used to be. Sebastian helped me carry the food to the table.

'Okay, get stuck in,' I said.

'This looks beautiful. Thank you for inviting me, Mrs Dyson,' Natasha said.

'Call me Charlie, Natasha, and no problem at all.'

Natasha hadn't said much since she had arrived, but she opened up at the dinner table and talked about herself, her job at the bank, and how she had got to know Mitch.

'She worked for me at one point, Mom, at the bank, and I took advantage of her,' Mitch joked.

'Mitch, that's not funny,' I said.

Sebastian laughed along with Mitch, typical men.

'Only joking, Mom, lighten up,' he said.

Natasha laughed. 'In your dreams, big boy; it was me who took advantage of you. I seduced you into a relationship.'

Natasha certainly knew how to put Mitch in his place. I liked her a lot.

The rest of the afternoon was full of laughter and fun. The kids enjoyed it, and it was so enlightening to see how happy they were. We talked a lot about when the baby comes.

I'd like you there, Mom, at the birth with Chris,' Summer said.

I was so delighted to hear that; the perfect news for a mom to hear to be present at the birth of their first grandchild.

Sebastian and I agreed to buy the cot and the pram. Mitch agreed to buy car seat and steriliser. Summer was thrilled.

The afternoon flew by, and before we knew it, it was time for them to leave. They all had work the next day, and come to think of it, that included me. We all kissed and hugged each other tightly; it was the best family reunion we could have hoped for. All safe and so much to look forward to.

Chapter 22
Back To Work

Sunday night wasn't great. I got worked up in the evening about work. I woke up about 2.30 am with hot sweats. I pulled off the quilt, but the sweats continued. I thought about work and wondered what it would be like. I got up at 3.00 am and was really sick. I remember holding my hair back whilst sitting over the toilet, throwing up. Sebastian was fast asleep so completely oblivious to it.

I didn't manage to go back to sleep and got up around 5.30 am. I pondered around getting the meal ready for the evening and ironing. The only difference today, we hadn't set the alarm as Sebastian didn't need to get up. I stopped downstairs, drinking tea for a while so as not to awake Sebastian. At around 7.00 am, I went up for a shower. After a shower, I opened my wardrobe to decide what to put on. I chose an outfit I usually wore a lot for work; it was a navy dress with a cream jacket.

I went into the bathroom to get dressed so as not to wake Sebastian. I pulled the dress on, pulling it up from my feet first. It felt a bit tight, and as I tried to do the zip up from the back, I realised I could no longer get in the dress.

'For fuck sake,' I said to myself.

I went back to my wardrobe and grabbed a few outfits. Everything I tried on either didn't fit or I looked fat. I was sweating trying on different outfits. I'd put the Covid stone on! I looked in the mirror, my face was so red, and my hair was everywhere. Why had I bothered doing my hair? I thought. I felt like jumping back in the shower.

Sebastian woke and slowly walked to the bathroom, naked as usual.

'There's clothes everywhere, Charlie. What's going on?'

'Nothing, just go back to bed.'

'What's up with you? Got out of bed the wrong side or something?' he asked.

'Nothing fits me?'

Sebastian shouted from the bathroom, 'Charlie, you had all day yesterday to sort out an outfit for today.'

'I didn't have all day yesterday at all. We had the kids, remember, and Gemma and John before that,' I shouted back.

I added, 'If you'd helped more with the dinner, I may have had time to get sorted for work.'

'Gees, Charlie, you are unbelievable. I asked yesterday what you wanted me to do, so don't blame everyone else if you're so disorganised,' he shouted back.

I ignored him and eventually got the zip up on a dress I'd fitted into. I popped my head round the bathroom door. Sebastian was sitting on the toilet.

'I'm off; see you later.'

'You not having breakfast?' Sebastian asked.

'No, not got time now. Anyway, it's not going to hurt me the weight I've put on. I need to cut back on the calories and carbs.'

'Cutting back on the prosecco might help,' he said.

Sebastian always had to have a dig about my weight and what I should eat and drink. I didn't respond; if I had, we'd have got into a row.

I left the house and drove to work. It felt strange pulling on to the carpark. There weren't many cars parked. Usually, it's half full by the time I get to work. I walked across to the office, my heart was pounding. I had butterflies. It was the not knowing what to expect after all this time.

There was someone from HR waiting to greet me.

'Morning, Charlie, lovely to see you. We are having a welcome back session first. There's a sanitiser here if you want to sanitise your hands first, then go into the big meeting room and take a chair. We'll start shortly, just waiting on a few more people,' she said.

'Okay, thanks,' I replied.

I sanitised my hands and headed for the meeting rooms. The doors were wedged wide open, and chairs had been placed leaving gaps between them for social distancing. There was already about twelve people in the room. I took a seat whilst waving to people and shouting hello. It all appeared very organised and controlled.

Shortly after, a few more people entered the room, including Joe. I didn't know where everybody else was. I couldn't see any of my team. Joe stood in the front to address us.

'As you are all aware, this has been unprecedented times for all of us and extremely difficult for us to operate as a business. It's good to see that you are all here safe and well. The business has adopted a two-phase plan to get things moving again. The first phase is survival, and the second phase is recovery. In phase one, we have taken the decision to only bring several people off furlough back into the business, which is everyone in this room. We have a big mountain to climb stabilising the business for the future, which is why we only have a several number of people to start. The sales team in this room is key to our success. We need to start to get orders into the system so that we can move to phase two, the recovery phase, and bring others back to work. I know we can do it. Are there any questions?' Joe asked.

The room was silent; you could hear a pin drop. Now, I know why my team wasn't in the room and only a few from other departments, more from the sales team.

Joe continued, 'Okay, no questions. Please feel free to ask me any at any point. I'm now going to hand over to Matt.'

Matt was our health and safety office. He stood from his chair and went to the front.

'I'll keep this short, but I wanted to brief you on what we've done as a business to address the Covid-19 guidelines. Firstly, you will see around the building several sanitisers, please sanitise and wash your hands regularly, in particular when you arrive in the office. All the doors are wedged open for a reason, to avoid you touching the handles. Please, do not close them. Some desks in the office have yellow tape on them; do not sit at those desks. We have tried to keep a desk free to each desk used to social distance amongst employees. All the offices have had a deep clean and will continue to be regularly cleaned. There is a register on the front desk. Can you please sign in and out each day for us to keep a record in case of any eventuality needed to track and trace. Finally, if you have any symptoms of Covid-19 or are contacted by the track and trace system, let us know immediately.'

Wow, that seemed to be a bit scary but sensible. Everyone left the room and went to the office. My desk was one that didn't have tape on it. Thank goodness for that, I thought. It felt odd not having my team, a bit lonely.

Joe asked for a meeting with me at 11.00 am. The memories of him shouting at me came flooding back. I hoped he wasn't going to be like that again.

As it turned out, he wasn't too bad. He explained that the business couldn't afford to bring everyone back at once until we'd got a sales pipeline of orders and cash looked strong. He asked me if I would keep the finance department ticking over and do a revised financial forecast and cash flow. He wanted to consider having a CBILS loan (Coronavirus Business Interruption Loan) from the bank and would need my support if that was the case. Finally, he said it was okay for me to work from home if I wanted and use the office as and when. This time, Joe was very civilised and reasonable.

After the meeting, I went through all the post for the finance department, actioned some of the mail, and got myself organised. Before I knew it, the day was over.

I got home around six'ish. Sebastian was watching some sport on TV with a beer.

'How'd it go?' he asked.

'Yea, okay. What you been up to all day?'

'Nothing much, had a workout, went for a run, did the lawns and prepared a few nutritional plans ready for next week.'

'Good, good, what's for dinner?' I asked, knowing full well he hadn't prepared anything.

Sebastian never turned his head from the TV. 'Great goal, get in there, errr, don't know, Charlie, what do you fancy to eat?'

'I've been at work all day, Sebastian; you could have got some dinner prepared for when I got home.'

Sebastian sighed. 'All you do, Charlie, is moan at me. I've done the lawns and cleaned up, but nothing's ever good enough. Be nice for you to come in and comment on what I have done.'

'But you've been home all day, I haven't, I replied.

'Right, what do you want to eat?' he asked.

'Well nothing now you put it like that. I'll do myself a sandwich and make do with that.'

I left him watching the sport, drinking beer, and made myself a ham and cheese toastie. After, I'd eaten, I opened a bottle of prosecco and took it upstairs with me to have a hot bath. I'd only been back at work a day, and things appeared to back as they were. After a bath, I put on some comfy pj's and got in bed. I put my headphones on and listened to some music on my phone whilst drinking the rest of the prosecco. I must have fell asleep because I didn't hear or notice Sebastian come to bed. I woke up about 2.00 am very hot and sweating; my head was also banging. I got up to get a glass of water and washed my face to cool myself down. Sebastian was fast asleep, snoring. I took a few painkillers and sat downstairs for a while. Once my headache had gone and I cooled down, I went back to bed. I lay awake for ages and couldn't get back off to sleep. In the end, I got up at 5.00 am. I decided to go into the office and not work from home to avoid Sebastian. He was starting to annoy me. I knew we would row if I stayed home.

CHAPTER 23

NORMAL LIFE

The rest of the week carried on the same as the Monday. I went to the office all week and struggled to find work outfits in my wardrobe to fit me. I got on the scales and weighed myself. To my horror I had gained ten pounds since before lockdown. This depressed me; no wonder I couldn't fit in my clothes. How could I gain that much weight so fast? I wanted to cry when I saw the scales. I didn't tell Sebastian. I didn't want him to think he had a fat wife. I felt embarrassed with myself that I had put that much weight on, especially as he worked out all the time and looked very fit. I had set myself a goal to lose two pounds a week to get it off.

The hot sweats and sleepless nights continued. By the end of the week, I was exhausted from lack of sleep. This made me irritable and argumentative. Sebastian and I bickered over silly things. I started to prepare my outfits for the next day on the evening; it was a chore to do it, but it saved so much time in a morning, plus I didn't disturb Sebastian in bed. Another benefit was my hair didn't get messed up in the morning trying different outfits on.

Saturday was the day the gyms opened; Sebastian was thrilled. He had made a flyer on the computer to promote himself and planned to go out to the gyms to promote himself. He left around 8.00 am and didn't come back until 8.30 pm. I can't believe I have a husband who is a personal trainer and nutritional diet planner and here was me desperate to lose weight but felt awkward to ask for Sebastian's help. All a bit mad really, I thought. I had tried hard all week, skipping breakfast, and only eating salad. My only problem was the prosecco!

I enjoyed having the Saturday to myself. Summer popped over and we had a good catch up. I had a bottle of prosecco whilst Summer visited.

'You can see a bit of a bump now, Mom, look,' she said as she lifted her top over her belly.

I couldn't see anything, but I didn't tell her that. 'Oh, yes, you can see it.'

'I'm eight weeks this week, Mom.'

I tapped her on the belly. 'Soon be time for your first scan.'

'I reckon it's a girl,' she said smiling.

'I reckon a boy,' I replied.

'Well as long as it's healthy, Mom.'

'Too true, Summer. Your dad and I are so pleased. Who'd have thought I'd have a grandchild at fifty.'

We spent the rest of the time looking at cots and nursery equipment on the internet. She looked so happy. I remember being like that when Sebastian and I found out I was pregnant.

I spoke with Mitch on the phone. He appeared to be all loved up and happy that he could now go to the pub and meet his mates.

I spent the rest of the afternoon listening to music, in and out the garden drinking prosecco. I must admit, I felt a bit tipsy by the time Sebastian arrived home. I remembered the last time I'd felt tipsy in the field; that seemed a distant memory.

Sebastian arrived back buzzing.

'Great to back in the gym, Charlie, love my job. Had a good catch up with some old clients and got plenty of new ones who have put the Covid stone on.'

'Great. I've had some lovely time with Summer; she popped over.'

'Oh, that's nice. You been drinking?'

'Yes, I have, why?' I asked.

'Nothing, you seem a bit tipsy. What's for dinner?' he asked.

Now, he knows the feeling of when I've come home to no dinner.

'I haven't done anything yet. What would you like?'

'It's okay, Charlie. I'll do myself a can of tuna with some salad. Got to watch the calories now I'm back at work.'

That's not how I would have responded, I thought. Maybe it was just me.

I got up Sunday and felt sick; it must have been all the prosecco I drank. I didn't want Sebastian to see me, so I went downstairs to throw up in the bathroom. I sat on the floor in the toilet for about a half hour with my head down the toilet. Eventually, the sickness stopped, and I went back upstairs to weigh myself. I couldn't believe to see that I had put on another pound. I sat on the toilet and cried. I'd hardly eaten all week; what I had eaten I had just vomited back up.

I had made my mind up not to eat anything at all on Sunday, plus I didn't feel right. I still had a sicky feeling that I couldn't shake off. I lay on the sofa most of the day in my PJ's. I didn't even cook a Sunday lunch. Sebastian was fine with it; we seemed to have eaten separate over the last week since I'd been back at work. Sebastian worked out again and prepared his very healthy dinners.

In the afternoon, I kept thinking about my weight gain, then a thought crossed my mind. I must be due for my period; that's why I've put a few pound on this week and feel tired and depressed. I tried to think back to my last period as I couldn't remember when it was. I remembered I'd had my ultrasound scan and internal on the 24th of June, so I knew my period wasn't then.

I tried so hard to think about when my period was after the scan. It was now Sunday 26th July. I must have had a period between the scan and now or due on my period. I thought back to all the sexual encounters Sebastian and I had had during lockdown and the time between my scan and now. I could not remember any intermittent bleeding or a period.

'Okay, think back, Charlie,' I thought.

I remembered at the scan telling them it had been two weeks since my last period, which would have been around the 9th / 10th of June, working it back. I must have had another period between then and now.

'Right, Charlie, think, think to all of sex you've had and when there was a gap,' I said to myself.

I remembered the field sex, which was the week of the 6th of July, last week we had Gemma and John and had sex, so it wasn't then. Those two weeks were ruled out. My scan was the 24th of June, and I knew it wasn't then. My brain went into overdrive. I don't think I'd had a period since the 9th / 10th June; in fact, the more I thought, the surer I was.

How could it have been this long without me not realising? I thought.

That was over six weeks ago!

I got my iPad and searched for what can cause a missed period. It came up with the following results:

+ Pregnancy
+ Stress
+ Sudden weight loss
+ Being overweight
+ Doing too much exercise
+ Taking the contraceptive pill
+ The menopause
+ Polycystic ovary syndrome (PCOS)

Pregnancy was top of the list; surely, I couldn't be pregnant at my age?

I examined each one carefully. Stress, well, maybe, but not during lockdown. Sudden weight loss, a definite no.

Being overweight, yes. I clicked on the link to read on further and read, *Your GP may refer you to a dietitian if you're overweight, with a BMI of 30 or more, and it's affecting your periods.*

That ruled that out. I have a BMI of 26. I knew this because Sebastian was obsessed with BMI and regularly checking mine.

I ruled out doing too much exercise. I only walked and did a few body pump sessions. I wasn't obsessed like Sebastian.

The contraceptive pill didn't apply to me.

The menopause, may be, I clicked on it to read more: *You may start missing periods as you approach the menopause. This is because oestrogen levels start to decrease, and ovulation becomes less regular. After the menopause, your periods stop completely.*

The menopause is a natural part of ageing in women, which usually happens between the ages of 45 and 55. The average age for a woman to reach the menopause is 51 in the UK.

This could apply to me, in the age bracket and been here before with this one. Sebastian is convinced I'm in the menopause and mentions it regularly.

Finally, on the list, polycystic ovary syndrome, hadn't got a clue was that was, so clicked on the link: *Polycystic ovaries contain a large number of harmless follicles, which are underdeveloped sacs in which eggs develop. If you have PCOS, these sacs are often unable to release an egg, which means ovulation does not take place.*

PCOS is thought to be very common, affecting about 1 in every 10 women in the UK. The condition is responsible for as many as one in three cases of stopped periods.

I ruled this out for now; this would have been picked up at my scan if there was an issue.

Menopause appeared to be the obvious reason. I still found it hard to accept the menopause, but it must be. This was the first time I accepted I could be going through the menopause. On that, Sebastian walked into the lounge and sat on the other sofa.

'What are you looking at?'

'Nothing special, just browsing holidays.'

'Holidays? I doubt we'll get anywhere this year with Covid.'

'We might, Sebastian; things are starting to open up again, and we've still got our vouchers with Tui from the turkey holiday that never happened.'

I decided to keep it to myself and not tell Sebastian about my period; it was for the best. I didn't want him worrying. I deleted the page on the iPad and deleted it from the history. I clicked on the TUI site and had a brief look at holidays.

'Turkey is not too bad in terms of price for September, thinking of my fiftieth.'

'Well, you need to decide what to do, Charlie, for your birthday. If we can get away, great.'

'Hmmm, I'll keep my eye on it. We have time booked off work for my birthday so we can book it last minute if we want.'

Sebastian shrugged. 'Yea, it's up to you.'

In the afternoon, we went shopping to the supermarket. We needed to get some food in ready for the week ahead; it was more difficult to go in the week now we were both back at work. From this weekend, we still had to wear face masks in shops. It was awful. I felt claustrophobic, and I found it difficult to breathe and talk. I was pleased I only had to wear it for shopping and not in a job where you had to wear it all day. There wasn't much of a queue to get in the supermarket, which was great.

We found Sunday afternoons to be the quietest. The supermarket still operated a one-way system around the store. A bit of pain if there was only one thing you wanted from a particular aisle, but we learned to live with it. This had been the new normal way of shopping for months. We walked down the toiletry isle to pick up some toiletries and heard a voice shout, 'Charlie, Sebastian, how the hell are you both?'

We turned to see Lewis. Lewis was a good friend of Sebastian's; they went to school together and used to work out together at the gym before we met at college. Lewis was a good-looking guy, tall and handsome, and he knew it. Lewis always had women at his feet, even now. He was very muscular with the hugest biceps I'd ever seen. He was well groomed and always looked immaculate.

I remember once having a crush on Lewis; Sebastian had no idea. It was one summer when the kids were young, and we had a BBQ. Lewis was single at the time; he was a bit of a player with women in his younger days. He wore the tightest denim shorts ever around his bum and bits! His penis looked huge in the shorts, and he flirted with it. He wore a tight t-shirt showing off his muscles. He looked like a male model. I remember going into the kitchen to get some mayo for the burgers. Lewis followed me in to get a cold beer out of the fridge. He had to squeeze past me to get to the fridge. I remember him putting his hands on my hips as he squeezed past me from the back. All I could feel was his body against mine as he did so, slowly brushing himself against me. He knew exactly what he was doing. I thought of him in those tight shorts as he did so.

'Bet you like a bit of thick mayo, Charlie,' he said to me as he got the beer out of the fridge. I felt myself getting red with embarrassment. He turned and winked and squeezed back past me again. I couldn't get it off my mind the rest of the afternoon; every time I looked over at him, I caught him looking at me. There was definitely chemistry between us. That night, I dreamt of being in bed with Lewis and having the most fantastic sex, trying all sorts of positions. I couldn't believe what I'd dreamt when I woke up. I hadn't ever imagined sleeping with anyone else before.

I would never have had an affair. Sebastian would never have forgiven me. That was one thing we always agreed with each other, if either of us slept with someone else it would be over; we couldn't forgive each other. I remember the time when I thought Sebastian was having an affair with Sarah on Facebook. I'm not sure I could have forgiven him if it had been true. Luckily for Sebastian, it was Lewis who he had reconnected with first.

'Lewis, we haven't seen you for ages. We're good, thanks, how are you?'

'I'm good, thanks, just doing a bit of shopping, and how's my Charlie doing?'

Even today, I felt myself redden in the face. 'I'm good, Lewis; you're looking well.' Lewis married a very pretty blonde girl, had two children, then got divorced about five years ago. Sebastian never elaborated, but I believe he had an affair and his wife found out. I wasn't surprised at all.

Sebastian and Lewis continued to chat for a while about the gym and old times. We started to get dirty looks and tutting from other shoppers as three of us stood chatting in the middle of the toiletry aisle. Probably not the best idea given social distancing, so I left them to it and carried on down the aisle with the trolley.

'Nice to see you, Lewis, hope to see you soon. I'll carry on, Sebastian, to get the shopping, we're blocking the aisle and getting dirty looks.'

'Okay, babe, I'll catch you up in a minute. I just want to exchange numbers with Lewis.'

Sebastian hadn't called me babe for well over a week. I think he had done it for Lewis's benefit. I wondered if he had noticed my face had gone red and the chemistry between us. I hoped not.

As I walked down the aisle, I stopped to pick up some shampoo. I slightly turned to look back at Sebastian and Lewis down the aisle. Lewis had moved his position so that Sebastian had his back to me, and he was facing down the aisle towards me. I could see him staring down to me as Sebastian messed with his phone. Gosh, this was all I needed right now. Lewis back in our lives. I didn't need any more complications in my life.

As I reached the end of the aisle, I got to the baby products, nappies, wipes, and milk. This reminded about by missed period. The thoughts of Lewis soon willowed away; my mind had moved onto my missed period. There was a mother in front of me with a young child no older than the age of three I'd have said. The child was screaming, and her mother was trying to reason with her. The child threw her dummy on the floor. Her mom picked it up and started shouting at her. This made the child cry even more.

The thought crossed my mind. What if I'm pregnant? How could I ever go through all this at my age? What would Sebastian do? I started to feel sick again; it was the thought and panic that rushed through my body. I ushered off as fast as I could down the aisle past the women and child. I could hear the child screaming from quiet afar. I didn't even turn back to see if Lewis was still glaring at me.

At the bottom of the aisle, there was an open-spaced chemist. It had a counter at the front with all the drugs set back from the store. I stopped and gazed across the drug counter at the back. I spotted the pregnancy tests.

'Right. I'll get one and put this to bed once and for all,' I thought. I knew if I purchased one separate, I could disclose it in my bag.

There was an elderly lady in front of me getting a prescription. It seemed to take forever. The pharmacist handed her the prescription, then she was asking about other drugs. 'Come on,' I kept thinking; the last thing I wanted was Sebastian seeing it. Eventually, the elderly lady was served and left.

The pharmacist nodded to me. 'Can I help you?'

Just as I was about to ask for the pregnancy test, I heard Sebastian's voice behind me.

'Boo, what you are you getting?'

'Oh, err, some sickness pills; my tummy isn't great.'

The pharmacist was still looking at me. 'Can I have something for an upset tummy, please?'

'Is it sickness, I heard you say?'

'It is, yes.'

'I have some medication, but I just need to check. You're not pregnant, are you?'

Sebastian laughed. 'No, she isn't; we're going to be grandparents. We've had our time with kids, too old for that now.'

'Oh, congratulations; we have to ask the question because you shouldn't take this medication if you are.'

I felt a hot sweat come all over me. I wanted to burst into tears. If Sebastian only knew what was going on in my head and what I was really going to purchase. I watched the pharmacist put the tablets in a bag.

'Take three a day, if it's no better in three days, I suggest you get in touch with your GP.'

'Okay, thank you.' I paid and moved on swiftly. I wanted to get out of the supermarket as fast as I could. We only had a few more things to get then we were in the queue at the checkout. As we were putting the shopping on the conveyor belt, a voice popped up.

'Twice in one day.'

It was Lewis at the next check out. I smiled and thought just get me out of here. I'd had enough for one day.

Sunday evening was much calmer, and we sat and watched a film. Sebastian hadn't tried it on at all this weekend. If he was going to, that would have been the day. Well, that was the normal before lockdown. I tried to put the whole period thing out of my mind by drowning a bottle of prosecco.

The last week of July was normal. Sebastian was so happy to be at work. I worked more from home as Sebastian wasn't there and did more forecasting for Joe; can't say I enjoyed it, but it was a job. So many people were being made redundant in firms, so I guess I was lucky to be in work. I thought about going out to get a pregnancy test, but the chemist was local, and I worried that I'd bump into somebody I knew. Everybody knew everybody in the village we lived in. I chose to leave it for a while.

Two weeks had passed, and we hadn't had sex since the last time when Gemma and John came. Sebastian hadn't even tried. We were more or less back to where we were before lockdown; in fact, I'd have said even worse. We hardly spoke that week, ate separately, never had sex, and never told each other we loved each other. I changed our shopping day to Saturday's. The thought of bumping into Lewis again; he knew our shopping time after seeing us, and I had a sneaky feeling he would go at that time to deliberately bump into us.

CHAPTER 24
ᏚHE FINALE

August was here, and still no period. I started to panic; it had now been eight weeks since my period. I was still gaining weight and not able to lose any weight; however, I had drunk more and more alcohol worrying about things.

It worried me more and more that I could be pregnant. I looked up on the internet:

'The risk of pregnancy complications increases as the mother's age increases. Risks associated with childbearing over the age of fifty include an increased incidence of gestational diabetes, hypertension, delivery by caesarean section, miscarriage, preeclampsia, and placenta previa.'

I probably shouldn't have done this because it worried me more. I also looked up the menopause again and late periods:

'Throughout the menopausal transition, some subtle—and some not-so-subtle—changes in your body may take place. You might experience: irregular periods. As ovulation becomes more unpredictable, the length of time between periods may be longer or shorter, your flow may be light to heavy, and you may skip some periods.'

That must be it, I thought. It must be menopausal; it can't be pregnancy at my age.

As the days passed, I thought more and more about not having a period and got myself depressed and in a state. Sebastian was so happy with his job. I drank more and more as the depression sank in, and I put a few more pounds on. I wished we didn't have the internet at times like this; it too easy to self-diagnose things.

The hot sweats and sleepless nights continued. I had mornings when I was sick. It was early morning on Saturday 8th August, I was sick in the bathroom downstairs, and Sebastian heard me. He came downstairs into the bathroom to me.

'Are you okay?'

'Yes, I'm fine.'

He left the bathroom and went into the kitchen. I cleaned myself up and went into him.

'Charlie, I've noticed you are drinking far too much; that's what's making you sick, you need to sort it out.'

'Stop telling me what to do, Sebastian.'

'Well, it's out of hand. You drank two bottles of prosecco last night in no time.'

'Well, it was Friday. I don't have work today, so what's the problem? I'm not hurting you?'

'Charlie, you're hurting yourself. I hate to see you like this. What's wrong, is it work?'

I started to fill up with tears. 'It's you, not work. We haven't had sex for weeks. I know I'm overweight, you don't show me any affection or anything. Our marriage is non-existent, Sebastian.'

Sebastian stood in silence and stared at me as the tears rolled down my face.

'Babe, come here.' He held me in his arms. 'You've been so difficult again as late. You've been drinking and getting more and more depressed. I never know what mood you're going to be in. You're obsessed that you're overweight. I don't know what's going on in your head, tell me, and I can help.'

'Well, there's…' I paused.

'There's what?' Sebastian asked as he kissed my head with his arms still around me to comfort me.

I paused again. 'Well, there's the menopause, and I think it's that.'

This was so what I wanted and hoped it to be. I still didn't have the nerve to tell him about my periods.

'Charlie, I'm here for you. Call the doctor on Monday and get some help. There's medication you can have today for it. HRT or whatever they call it. You don't have to suffer like this.'

Sebastian held my head; one hand on each side of my face and wiped my tears away

'I love you and don't want you to suffer like this. Promise me, you will call the GP Monday morning.'

I nodded and blew my hair off my face where it had stuck to the wetness from my tears.

'I have to go to work today, babe. I've got a busy one with clients. Why don't you book that holiday in Turkey for your birthday next month? It will do you good to have something to look forward to.'

'I'll have a look.'

'Okay, Charlie, are sure you're going to be okay?'

'Yes, don't worry about me. I'm fine.'

Sebastian walked off to get his gym kit ready for work.

'Oh, Charlie. Lewis called last night. I promised him when we met in the supermarket, we'd have a proper meet up and a bite to eat. I've asked him for Sunday lunch tomorrow, is that okay?'

My heart sank. 'Errr, yea, no problem.'

As if my life wasn't complicated enough, I could do without Lewis being at the house right now. Sebastian walked back with his gym bag and kissed me on the cheek.

'See you later babe, get that holiday booked.'

He left for work. I sat on the sofa thinking about Lewis. I imagined what it was going to be like, I knew he would flirt with me, and I would have to resist myself from flirting back. There was something about him that attracted me to him. He was like a magnet. The way things had been the past few weeks between Sebastian and I, some attention would not go amiss. I thought back to the dream I had of having great sex with him. I thought to myself, I bet he's really good in bed and very manly. I started to think of what it would be like having sex with him. This was getting dangerous. I had to put all of these thoughts out of head, for goodness sake, I had too much other stuff going on.

I then thought about my missed period again; it was now over eight weeks since my last one. I had turned into a living wreck thinking about it. I decided it was time to put my mind at ease and buy a pregnancy test.

I got ready and went off to do the shopping on my own while Sebastian was at work. This was the ideal opportunity and the first I had had to get a pregnancy test. I got my mask on and set off. I got my usual shopping and headed down the toiletry aisle to the pharmacy at the bottom. There was one person in front of me. I waited and looked over at the shelf at the pregnancy tests whist they were being served. I started to feel butterflies in my stomach. I looked round to make sure there was no one I knew.

'Can I help you?'

I muttered quietly under my mask so as no one else could hear me. 'Can I have one of those pregnancy tests, please.' I pointed to them.

'Sorry, I can't hear you well. Was it a pregnancy test you said?'

I nodded.

I felt so embarrassed; the pharmacist must have thought you are too old for one of these. I looked again to check no one was around. I wanted the pharmacist to put it in the bag as soon as possible.

She put the test in a paper bag and handed it to me.

'Thank you; it's for my daughter.'

She smiled at me. I paid and put it in my handbag.

My face was flushed and red. I felt a hot sweat coming on and the mask made it worse, I could hardly breathe. I got the rest of the shopping as quick as possible and left for home.

I hadn't long been home and put the shopping away when my mobile rang. It was Summer.

'HI, Mom, how are you?'

'I'm all good, Summer. How are you feeling?'

'All good, Mom. I've had my thirteen-week scan appointment come through for the 13th of August.'

'Oh, that's good.'

'You don't sound overly excited, Mom.'

The thought of babies and hospitals all went through my head

'No, I'm overjoyed, Summer. I've just got a lot on my mind at the moment. Do you get a picture with this one?'

'Yes, I'll get you one. Chris can't come in with me now due to the coronavirus. I have to go on my own.'

'Oh, that's a shame. I bet he's gutted.'

'He is, but there's still no visitors at all allowed in the hospital.'

'Gosh, that's awful for families.'

'What are you and Dad up to this weekend?'

'Your dad's at work today, and tomorrow we've got Lewis coming for dinner. Don't know whether you remember him. He was your dad's friend from school.'

'Gosh, yes, I do remember him. He was the nice-looking guy. You haven't seen him for ages.'

'That's the one; we bumped into him at the supermarket the other week, so your dad's reconnected with him'

'He always had a crush on you, Mom.'

I felt myself blush. 'No, he didn't.'

'He so did, Mom. Charlie this and Charlie that; he couldn't take his eyes off you. He undressed you with his eyes,' she joked.

'Stop it, Summer, and don't be ridiculous if your father heard you talking like that.'

'He reminds me of Mr Grey out of that book 50 Shades of Grey.' She laughed. 'Be careful, Mom.'

'Your dad can be like that.'

'Dad? You are joking, he's as straight as anything. Couldn't see him into bondage or anything.'

'Summer, let's change the subject. What are you up to this weekend?'

'Nothing much. Chris is working today and finishing off some decorating tomorrow. I'm working tomorrow.'

They were always decorating.

We chit-chatted for another five minutes about covid-19. Spain, France, and Italy had seen an increase in cases over the past few weeks.

'Have you heard the news, Mom, about Bromsgrove?'

'No, not listened to it for a few days, why?'

'It's one of the worse affected area's for increases in cases in Covid-19. They are making a decision early next week whether to put the area into lockdown.'

'You're joking?'

'No, I thought you'd heard it. We've had a spike in the hospital again.'

'That will please your dad; he's only just gone back to work.'

'Hmmm, a second wave is inevitable, Mom. I've got to go, Mom. There's somebody at the door.'

'Okay, Summer, look after yourself, love you lots.'

'Love you, Mom.'

I spent the rest of the afternoon deep in thought wondering what the future held and what my destiny was going to be.

I got the pregnancy test out of my bag and read the instructions. I read how the test works and how a line would appear if it were positive. The instructions said that first thing in the morning was best to get an accurate reading; the very first pee of the day. My heart pounded as I contemplated doing it now and my stomach turned over sick with worry, my legs felt like jelly.

Lots of questions and thoughts went through my mind.

What would I do if I were pregnant? Would I keep it? Is this a reincarnation of the baby I lost? Would I have to have a c-section again? How would I tell Sebastian? How would Sebastian feel? What would it be like to have a child at fifty, and I could I cope with it? I remembered Sebastian saying to me in the field when we had sex, 'So proud we are going to be grandparents. You've done well bringing up the kids. This is where we can enjoy having grandkids to stay but can give them back when we've had enough.'

Then I remembered Sebastian saying to the pharmacist in the supermarket when she asked if I was pregnant, 'No, she isn't. We're going to be grandparents. We've had our time with kids, too old for that now.'

Sebastian wouldn't want any more children, I thought. He had plans to retire at fifty-five and do other stuff; he enjoyed his life too much.

Would our marriage survive through this? Will it survive anyway? Would Sebastian give me an ultimatum? Then there's the kids, how would they feel? How would Summer feel me having a baby the same age as her child? How would I feel having a baby and grandchild the same age? It's a big commitment at fifty. I thought back to the screaming child in the supermarket and sighed. How would I cope with menopause and a child? What about my job? Was all this lust of sex in lockdown worth it?

Is it the menopause and not a pregnancy? I thought. At least if it were menopause, I could go to the doctor on Monday and get some help like Sebastian suggested.

I held the test in my hand and stared at it contemplating whether to do it. After a few minutes, I decided not to do it until the morning. I had got myself worked up getting the test, and if it wasn't accurate or I messed up, I couldn't pop out to get another one. I only had the opportunity today to purchase one. It was best to wait until morning, be accurate, and get my answer once and for all.

I put the test back in my bag, ready for the morning.

I then started to think about tomorrow and Lewis coming for lunch. Again, more questions and deep thoughts.

Why was there chemistry between us? How did Summer pick it up? Was it obvious? Did Sebastian have an incline?

Why did I think and fantasise of having sex with him? Did Lewis think about sex? How would he perform? Could I resist him if he tried something on with me? How deep were our feelings?

What would he wear tomorrow? I bet he would wear something sexy. Perfectly groomed. Was this fate and had Lewis come back into our lives for a reason?

This then brought me onto Sebastian.

How would he feel if he knew my thoughts about Lewis? If I allowed anything to happen between Lewis and I, would he end the marriage? Was our marriage right anyway? We've gone back to no intimacy and no sex as late. Sex was scarce before lockdown. What happened to us during lockdown? What was all that lust and sex about? We tried all kinds of positions and places. Why couldn't it be like that all the time? Was it me? Is this normal for a couple of our age? Does Sebastian think I'm unattractive or fat as I've aged? What do we have in common?

I finally thought about the coronavirus.

What if we had a second wave? Would we go into lockdown again? Would we be safe? I would miss the kids again. Would we go back to our sexual fantasies having sex like rabbits in a second lockdown? What about our jobs in a second lockdown? Would we be furloughed again?

Sebastian wanted me to book a holiday for my fiftieth. How could I do this with all this going on and so many unanswered questions? I knew I would have to make an excuse as to why I hadn't booked it. What would my fiftieth be like and where would I be?

So many questions and thoughts I pondered on. I didn't have the answers, but one thing I did know, tomorrow would be the start of a new chapter in my life. I was about to start on a new path and my destiny would be determined. Tears rolled down my face. I was scared about the future; nobody likes change, so many unanswered questions for life after fifty.